Nuffield Primary Science

SCIENCE PROCESSES AND CONCEPT EXPLORATION

UNDERSTANDING SCIENCE IDEAS

A Guide for Primary Teachers

PUBLISHED FOR THE NUFFIELD FOUNDATION BY COLLINS EDUCATIONAL

NUFFIELD PRIMARY SCIENCE
Science Processes and Concept Exploration

Directors
Paul Black
Wynne Harlen

Deputy Director
Terry Russell

Project members
Robert Austin
Derek Bell
Adrian Hughes
Ken Longden
John Meadows
Linda McGuigan
Jonathan Osborne
Pamela Wadsworth
Dorothy Watt

Principal contributor to this book
Lesley Newson

Editors of this book
Derek Bell
Noel George

Other contributors to this book
John Barker
Jenny Begg
Annabel Batten
Sarah Codrington
R.W. Fairbrother
Anne Goldsworthy
Ralph Hancock
Andrew Hunt
Brenda Keogh
Jean Macqueen
Anne de Normanville
Stuart Naylor
Jonathan Osborne
Pat Palmer
Pamela Wadsworth

Published by Collins Educational
An imprint of HarperCollins*Publishers*
77–85 Fulham Palace Road
Hammersmith
London W6 8JB

www.**Collins**Education.com
On-line support for schools and colleges

First published 1997
Reprinted 1997, 1998, 1999, 2000

ISBN 0 00 310 018 9

Designed by Neil Adams, Grasshopper Design Company

Illustrations by Emma Holt, John Booth, Karen Tushingham,
Sally Neave, Jakki Wood, Gay Galsworthy

Cover artwork by Karen Tushingham

British Library Cataloguing in Publication Data
A catalogue record for this book is available from the British Library

You might also like to visit
www.**fire**and**water**.co.uk
The book lover's website

Printed and Bound by Printing Express Ltd., Hong Kong.

Contents

Introduction

Knowing the content is not all

Most teachers feel that, to teach a subject well, they themselves have to be comfortable with the subject. However, to be comfortable and effective teaching a subject requires more than just knowledge of the subject matter. Many different kinds of knowledge are needed. It is therefore important, in a book that aims to help teachers' own understanding of science, to put this in the context of other kinds of knowledge that teachers need and use in their work. We should also recognize the limitations of what can be done in a few pages in relation to the wide range of science ideas that primary teaching may involve.

Knowledge and the teacher's role

In the SPACE (Science Processes And Concept Exploration) approach to teaching science, the teacher's role is to help children develop their understanding, starting from the ideas they already have about the topic under study. In brief this role involves

- planning a topic or area of investigation around the development of understanding of key ideas and skills,
- starting the topic or investigation by giving children opportunities first to explore new materials, events and situations, and then to express their ideas about what they are exploring (You can read about these strategies for finding out children's ideas in the Nuffield Primary Science teachers' guides.),
- discussing with the children their reasons for holding their particular ideas,
- using one or more strategies (again listed in the teachers' guides) for helping children to develop their ideas, based on the nature of the children's ideas and how these relate to the key ideas the teacher has in mind,
- reviewing with the children the extent to which ideas have developed, and planning further experiences to take the development further.

In adopting such an approach to teaching and learning science, teachers particularly need knowledge and understanding of

- the key ideas so that they can identify good starting-points, know when children are hovering near to the scientific view or are still a long way from it, recognize blind alleys, and ensure that children encounter the experiences that will help them rethink their ideas,
- the process skills of science so that they can help children reflect on and test their ideas in a systematic manner.

Why do we need to understand key ideas?

We are not suggesting that teachers need understanding so that scientific ideas can be taught didactically. That could only lead to rote learning and would be severely damaging to children's confidence in their own ability to make sense of their experiences. One thing we know is that the only way children develop ideas they fully understand is through their own thinking. Teachers cannot do the thinking for them, neither can they short-circuit the learning process by presenting the key ideas for children to learn.

The key ideas are generalizations that link a range of experiences. From each of these experiences children will gain 'small' ideas relating to the particular contexts encountered. It is the aim of science education to give children these experiences, to enable children to form ideas that are meaningful to them and consistent with their experience, and to help them gradually to link their ideas to form bigger, more widely applicable, key ideas.

So we are not saying that teachers need to understand key ideas so that they can transfer them to children. What we are saying is that teachers need the understanding themselves so that they can recognize and promote relevant small ideas that can be linked to form bigger ones; so that they can ask questions that lead children to reveal and reflect on their ideas; so that they can provide relevant sources of information and other resources; and so that they can identify progress and the next steps that will take it further. These things cannot be done if teachers do not understand the key ideas they are aiming for.

Why do we need to understand the process skills of science?

We use science process skills (observing, measuring, hypothesizing, predicting, planning and carrying out investigations, interpreting, inferring, and communicating) to make sense of the evidence and information relating to the world around us.

Similarly, children use the process skills to test their ideas in the light of new experiences and evidence. By encouraging children to test and challenge their ideas, we can help them develop ideas that are more useful in understanding the world around them.

We should remember, however, that the way in which process skills are used is important – this determines the ideas that are developed from an activity. For example:

- if children observe only certain more obvious aspects of an object, they may miss vital information;
- if children suggest that something may happen but don't test to see if it does, they are left with ideas for which they have no evidence;
- if children plan and carry out a test that isn't 'fair', they will be drawing conclusions on the basis of suspect information.

In other words, if children use the process skills in a way that is unscientific they are not obtaining reliable evidence to test their ideas. Teachers need to realize what is involved in using these skills scientifically in order to help children use them.

In order to help children develop their understanding of concepts, we need to provide opportunities for them to make links between their own ideas and other alternatives. By making predictions, by gathering evidence through observing, by comparing and measuring to test these predictions, and by suggesting explanations based on their interpretation of the information available to them, children are being helped to develop ideas that make sense to them. In providing appropriate opportunities for children to test their ideas in this way, and by drawing their attention to relevant evidence, teachers can help children develop their ideas towards a more scientific understanding of different phenomena.

The importance of understanding the process skills of science is further emphasized because, as our ideas become more sophisticated and abstract, the means of testing needs to be more precise and better focused. We need to help children become more proficient in using the process skills so that, as their ideas develop, the testing of these ideas becomes more rigorous and reliable.

Understanding: a continuous process

Understanding is a continuous process that goes on throughout life. It is impossible to say that anyone achieves complete understanding. Think of the different understanding that, say, a 6-year-old, a 16-year-old, and a 26-year-old research chemist would have for the concept of 'dissolving'. For the child it might mean a solid becoming no longer visible when put in water. The 16-year-old may have linked several phenomena and envisage it as a process that depends on the nature of the two substances brought together. The chemist will link it to the molecular structure of these substances.

Where along this continuum of understanding should primary teachers be?

There is no simple answer to this question. As we have shown above, the function of teachers' own knowledge is to enable them to help children to advance their ideas by engaging in scientific exploration. Teachers worry about 'not knowing enough' when they think that teaching means that they must be able to answer children's questions and present accurate information. In practice, no-one could answer all the questions that the inquiring minds of children will raise, and indeed in many cases it would be wrong to attempt to answer them. Giving children facts that do not link into their own experience and thinking can deter them from asking questions, since they find they cannot understand the answers. So teachers have to respond in other ways to questions, turning them wherever possible into ones the children themselves can investigate.

This is not an argument against teachers developing their own understanding, but it is a reason for emphasizing broad principles that enable teachers to guide children's inquiries in fruitful directions. For primary teachers the appropriate level of understanding is that which enables them to make sense of and is consistent with the experiences of their pupils. They must see the links between the 'small' ideas that children will develop from particular experiences and the bigger key ideas.

Experience, supported by research, shows that teachers, as educated adults with a great deal of relevant experience, can quickly grasp broad principles of science at this level. Many teachers have, indeed, developed their own understanding by 'reading up' on topics or by talking to colleagues. Unfortunately the science books available are often written for another readership and are unsuitable for the purpose of developing primary teachers' understanding. This book is designed to provide ready access to discussion of the key ideas at the appropriate level, consistent with the philosophy of Nuffield Primary Science.

Look at each of these: is it living, has it never lived, or was it once living? What criteria have you used?

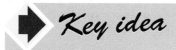

Key idea

Living things are distinguished from non-living things by their ability to carry out certain processes.

Children entering reception class have spent four years in a world in which the family cat cannot be treated like a teddy bear, in which insects might bite, grass has to be cut and flowers must not be trampled on. They have had to develop a practical system for sorting out living from non-living. As they learn more about life, such judgements become more difficult. Public debates about the disposal of frozen embryos and when it is acceptable to declare someone brain dead show that the greatest human minds supported by the latest scientific evidence can also have trouble deciding when something is alive.

Nevertheless, the first step in learning about living things has to be one of defining the basic properties of Life. Not surprisingly, some of these properties are the same as those used by pre-school children to judge what is alive.

 ## Children's ideas

Young children may have very different ideas about what is living. They tend to over-emphasize movement as a characteristic of living things and some may suggest that clouds and fire are alive.

All living things

- are able to move (and not just when something pushes them)

- are sensitive to stimuli (They react to some changes around them.)

- make more of themselves (by growing and developing and by reproducing to create new individuals)

- keep themselves separate from their environment (If you endanger this separateness by cutting or crushing a living thing, it will try to heal itself and if it is unsuccessful, it will die.)

- take in energy and materials from the environment (Some, such as animals, obtain energy from food from the environment. Others, such as plants, obtain energy from sunlight.) Many organisms also take in oxygen.

- release (excrete) waste materials into the environment

- are made up of one or more units called cells.

It is not immediately obvious that every item on this list applies to ALL living things, but some simple experiments can reveal more about the processes that go on in living things.

Plants do not seem to move or react to stimuli. However, if a house plant is turned so that its leaves face away from the window, the leaves will turn back to face the light once more in a matter of hours or days. This shows, not only that the plant can move, but that it is sensitive to the stimulus of light.

The dried seeds of the bean plant seem no more alive than a handful of pebbles, but if the seeds are placed in a moist environment where they can absorb water and oxygen, they will start behaving like living things.

A seed is alive because it has the potential for displaying all the properties of life. That potential can be destroyed by various means such as cooking or crushing the seed.

You cannot see a plant collecting up materials from the environment the way an animal does when it eats, but if you keep a plant in the dark so that it does not get energy from sunlight it cannot grow and may die. (See 'Staying alive' on pages 10–11.) Depriving it of water will also prevent its growth and cause it to die.

By doing experiments, both simple and very complex, scientists have been able to learn about the processes that go on inside living things and have discovered what makes them different from things that are not alive. They have found fundamental similarities between the inner workings of all living things, whether they be humans, oak trees or tiny single-celled bacteria.

Reflection

The similarities between the processes that occur in all living things provide the most convincing evidence that all living things are related and probably evolved from common ancestors – very simple organisms that formed billions of years ago.

Key idea

All living things are made up of one or more cells.

Although many children will have heard of germs, most will only be familiar with living things that are large enough to see. In fact, the vast majority of living things on Earth are far too small to see with the naked eye. Each one is a tiny but highly organized container of chemicals, called a cell. Larger organisms are multi-cellular. They are organized groups of many cells that work together with different cells specializing to perform different tasks.

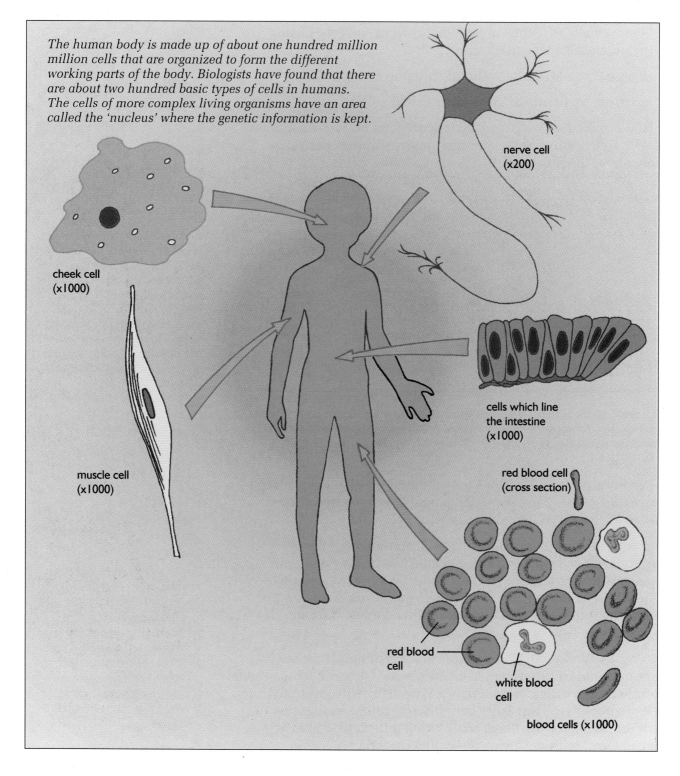

The human body is made up of about one hundred million million cells that are organized to form the different working parts of the body. Biologists have found that there are about two hundred basic types of cells in humans. The cells of more complex living organisms have an area called the 'nucleus' where the genetic information is kept.

nerve cell (x200)

cheek cell (x1000)

muscle cell (x1000)

cells which line the intestine (x1000)

red blood cell (cross section)

red blood cell

white blood cell

blood cells (x1000)

Cells are so complex that it may be useful to think of them as factories full of machines. The work of these microscopic factories is to carry out highly controlled, perfectly timed and extremely complex chemical reactions. As long as this work goes on, the cell is alive.

Like pieces of machinery, cells need a supply of energy. Unlike machines, cells maintain themselves, grow and reproduce. To do this, they need to bring in chemical raw materials and to dispose of the waste they make as they work. Every cell, whether it is part of a multi-cellular organism or living on its own, is surrounded by a thin skin, called a membrane. This acts as a barrier, keeping the mixture of chemicals inside the cell separate from the chemicals outside. It is also responsible for importing raw materials and exporting waste.

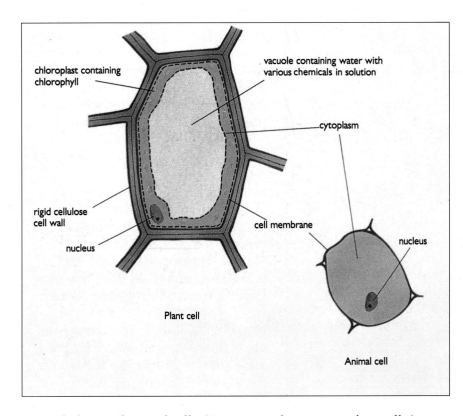

Typical plant and animal cells. (See page 11 for more on plant cells.)

Genetic information

The chemical machinery of a cell is built by the cell itself as it grows, and each cell needs to carry instructions for building this machinery. These instructions are coded into the structure of a chemical called deoxyribonucleic acid, or DNA for short. Biologists have found that the instructions are divided into units of information, which they call genes, and the entire blueprint for an organism is known as its genetic information.

As the chemical machinery of the cell works, the genetic information is consulted whenever instructions are needed for making new tools or machines. Complex multi-cellular creatures like humans have a vast amount of genetic information that is passed on from one generation to another – see page 14.

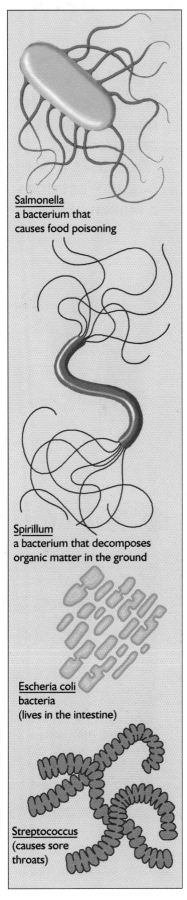

Bacteria consist of a single cell that is much smaller than animal or plant cells.
(Scale: x10 000)

3 > Staying alive

What does a plant need to stay alive and grow? What does a dog need? What does a human need?

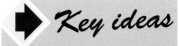 *Key ideas*

Living things need certain conditions to stay alive.

All living things need water and nutrients to grow. Many need oxygen. Green plants also need light and carbon dioxide.

Animals cannot make their own food, but plants can produce food (as sugars) from water and carbon dioxide in the presence of sunlight and chlorophyll. This process is called photosynthesis.

Living things can survive in a vast range of different conditions. Lichen can thrive on the rocky summits of mountains. Some bacteria make a living in the mud on the bottom of the deepest ocean trenches, miles beneath the surface. However, all living things have certain fundamental needs. They need a source of materials and they need a source of energy.

Getting energy

Living things get energy in two main ways:

- Absorbing energy from sunlight ('the plant way')
- Breaking down food chemicals ('the animal way').

It is convenient to think of these two methods of getting energy as 'the plant way' and 'the animal way', but the methods are not limited to plants and animals. Simpler organisms, including single-celled organisms, use these methods too. Also, not all of the organisms people think of as plants are able to get energy from sunlight. For example, mushrooms (which are fungi) obtain their energy by breaking down (or rotting) other living things.

Biologists often call living things that get energy by photo-synthesizing 'producers': they produce food that is eaten by other living things. Creatures that eat other living things are called 'consumers'. Mushrooms and other living things that get their energy by rotting dead material are consumers but they are also known as decomposers. (See pages 26–7.)

Getting energy 'the plant way'

The process that allows plants to get energy from light is called photosynthesis. This is a series of chemical reactions that uses light energy to bind chemicals together. Bright green chlorophyll has a key role in these reactions. Most green plants have special solar energy collecting organs called leaves. It is the chlorophyll in leaves that makes them green.

The pictures below show the structure of a leaf and the parts of the leaf cells that contain chlorophyll (chloroplasts).

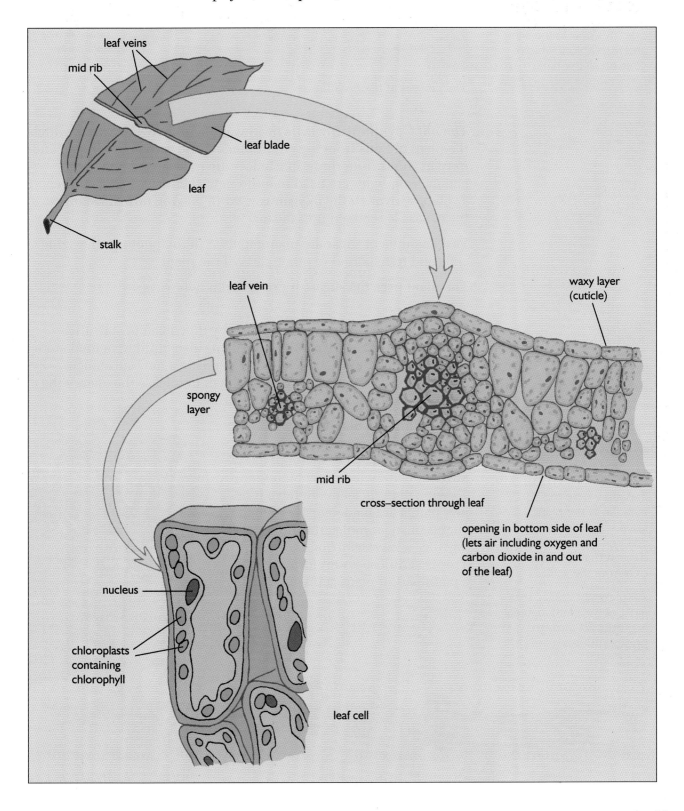

leaf veins

mid rib

leaf blade

leaf

stalk

leaf vein

waxy layer (cuticle)

spongy layer

mid rib

cross–section through leaf

opening in bottom side of leaf (lets air including oxygen and carbon dioxide in and out of the leaf)

nucleus

chloroplasts containing chlorophyll

leaf cell

Children's ideas

Older children often have the idea that plants 'breathe out' oxygen during the day and carbon dioxide at night.

They are confusing two quite different processes: photosynthesis, which operates only in the light, and respiration, which goes on all the time.

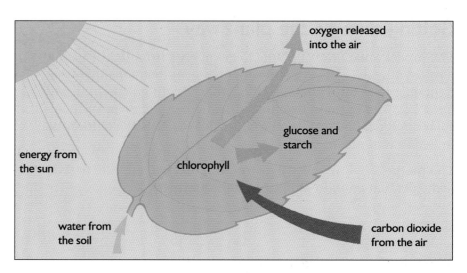

The process of photosynthesis

The photosynthesizing cells need water and carbon dioxide, which the plant obtains from the environment. The carbon, hydrogen and oxygen atoms from these substances are re-arranged and, using energy from light, are used to build new chemicals – sugars such as glucose. Not all the oxygen is used in making new substances: the excess is released into the air.

Vast amounts of sugar are manufactured in the photosynthesizing cells and transported to other parts of the plant.

The plant uses the sugars it produces in two ways:

1 As a 'food'
Plants use sugars to produce the energy they need to stay alive (see respiration on page 13). Most plants also build up a food store. They link sugar molecules together to create a new substance called starch. The starch is broken down to release the energy the plant needs for new growth in the spring.

2 As a building material
Plant cells can chemically process sugars to produce the marvellous range of materials from which the growing plant is made. Believe it or not, plants are made mostly of long chains of sugar molecules linked together with strong bonds. This is cellulose and it forms a main part of plant cell walls.

Children's ideas

If asked where the material of the plant comes from, many children and adults will suggest that it comes only from the soil.

Many do not realize that most of the plant material is produced through photosynthesis.

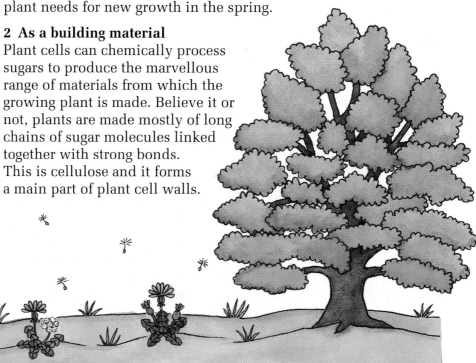

All made mostly of cellulose

Getting energy 'the animal way'

Most living things that cannot absorb energy from sunlight get the energy they need by consuming material that has been created by other living things. Put more simply: animals get their energy from the food they eat.

The process that allows cells to get energy from food is called respiration. Unlike photosynthesis, respiration is not carried out in specialized cells. Virtually all cells, including plant cells (see page 12), carry out respiration. In a sense, respiration allows cells to use their food like our machines use fuel.

Overall, respiration takes in food (especially sugars) and oxygen, and produces carbon dioxide and water, while providing energy to living cells. The carbon dioxide produced is released into the air. The water is either used by the body or released into the environment.

Obtaining nutrients

Living things do not just need a supply of energy to stay alive. They also need to take in certain materials that are essential to the construction of their cellular machinery. These are known as nutrients and include minerals such as compounds containing phosphorus, potassium, nitrogen and calcium.

The minerals that plants need dissolve in water, and plants take them in along with the water they absorb. It is these chemicals we supply when we feed, or fertilize, a plant, although the chemicals are naturally present in the water of fertile soil.

Animals obtain the nutrients they need mostly from their food. They need roughly the same substances as plants (compounds containing calcium, phosphorus and potassium, for example). They also need to take in a range of more complex chemicals – fats, proteins and carbohydrates – which plants make for themselves. Animals also need to import vitamins. A number of animal and plant diseases have been found to be caused by a lack of specific nutrients. The kinds of nutrients and the amounts needed vary from animal to animal.

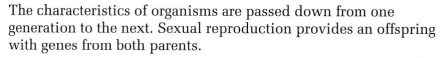

4 — Growth, development and reproduction

The characteristics of organisms are passed down from one generation to the next. Sexual reproduction provides an offspring with genes from both parents.

Living things are programmed with the ability to progress through a life cycle. This involves growing larger and developing different structures and abilities, and it involves reproducing to create new living things like themselves.

As with other life processes, understanding what the cells are doing is important to understanding growth, development and reproduction. The life cycle of the organism is programmed as part of the genetic information contained in each cell.

Cell division

Making new cells is fundamental to growth and this is done by a single cell dividing in two. The cell makes a copy of its genetic information and then, as the cell splits in two, a complete set of genetic instructions is provided for each new cell. In most single-celled creatures, bacteria for example, copying their genetic information and splitting in two usually constitute their entire life cycle. For multi-celled organisms such as animals and plants, it is rather more complicated.

Animal life cycle

An animal begins its life cycle as a single cell that divides many times to create a large multi-cellular organism. As the cells divide, the new cells created develop into different types of cells, each type specialized to perform certain jobs in the body. These cells organize themselves to form the different body tissues.

To reproduce, most animals make specialized reproductive cells that contain only a single edition of each of the instructions in the animal's library of genetic information. One cell from each of two individuals, male and female, unite to create a single cell containing a complete set of genetic instructions. These are made up from those of each parent, but are not identical to either parent. This is sexual reproduction.

Plant life cycle

Many plants also produce specialized reproductive cells that unite with those from other plants. In plants that we are most familiar with, this occurs in the flower.

As the flower develops, the reproductive cells form in the anther and ovary (see the diagram on page 15). Those in the anther develop into pollen, and those in the ovary develop into ovules. Once the pollen has developed, it is released from the anther. Some types of pollen are simply blown around by the wind. Others are transferred from plant to plant by insects.

Pollination:
flower shedding its pollen
flower being pollinated
flower developing into fruit

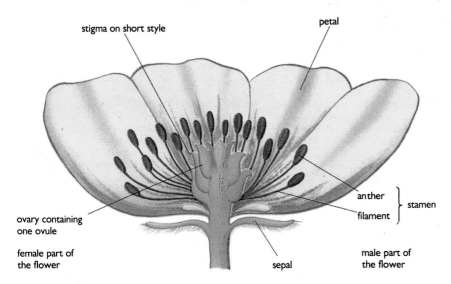

stigma on short style

petal

anther
filament
} stamen

ovary containing
one ovule

female part of
the flower

sepal

male part of
the flower

Buttercup flower

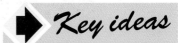

Key ideas

All living things grow but
this takes place gradually.

Living things reproduce
individuals of the
same kind.

If pollen lands on the ovary of another plant of the same species,
the genetic information in the pollen joins with the genetic
information of an ovule to create a cell with a new combination.
This develops into a seed, and in many species of plant, the ovary
that surrounds it ripens to form a fruit.

Plant seeds also contain a supply of food for the young plant to use
as it grows. Like animals, plants develop as they grow. Their cells
specialize to create tissues and structures that do specific jobs.

Plants differ from animals in that they have a greater capacity to
reproduce without using reproductive cells. This is because tissues
from many parts of the plant contain cells that are able to develop
into any of the cells that make up a plant. An entirely new plant
can grow from a small piece of a 'parent' plant. Strawberries,
willow trees and many other kinds of plants reproduce in this
way. This is asexual reproduction.

 ## Children's ideas

What do seeds contain? Children often think that they contain miniature
plants, waiting to grow.

 ## Reflection

Growth and reproduction is less flexible in animals than in plants.
If you want a small dog, you must start with the right puppy. You cannot
prune a Great Dane puppy in order to grow a bonsai Great Dane.

You can grow a new African violet from a single leaf. Human
reproduction cannot be accomplished by cutting off a finger and
sticking it in a pot.

How are you able to respond to stimuli?

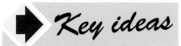

Key ideas

The senses – touch, smell, taste, sight and hearing – inform us of our surroundings.

Living things respond to changes in their environment.

Some things, such as drugs, alcohol and tobacco, can harm our health.

Reflection

Humans have a brain that allows us to process information from the environment in a much more complex way than other animals. We can consider many possible courses of action, create novel solutions to problems, and discuss our ideas with other humans.

In view of this it seems strange that we often behave far more irrationally than other animals. Many of us use tobacco, alcohol and other drugs even though we know they are harmful. We risk our own lives and those of our loved ones by driving too fast.

Living organisms are able to respond to stimuli from their environment. Their ability to move allows them to exploit their environment and avoid harm.

Even the simplest living things have some ability to detect what is going on around them and to react to it. Experiments have shown that bacteria move towards a source of food chemicals and away from a source of harmful chemicals.

Multi-cellular organisms have cells that are specialized to gather information from the environment. Information is communicated from cell to cell so the organism can respond in a co-ordinated way. For the cells of a multi-cellular organism to work together effectively, they must live as part of a well-supported structure. Both plants and animals have special tissues devoted to providing support to the rest of the body tissues.

Animal movement and support

Animals have specialized tissues, called muscles, which can get shorter (contract) very rapidly. They also have sense organs that gather information from the environment and nerves that transmit the information around the body. Even the simplest animals have a co-ordinating centre to process the information and control their response.

We tend to think of muscles as those things that ripple under the skin of a weightlifter, but muscles do far more in the body than move our limbs. The humans body contains literally millions of muscles, some very tiny. We are unaware of these muscles because we have little or no conscious control over them. Nevertheless, they are moving all the time. Muscles in the walls of our intestines push our food along as it is digested. Our heart is a muscle that contracts about once a second, every second of our lives.

A larger and heavier animal needs a stronger and more rigid supporting structure than a smaller animal. For example, the structure of a worm can be more flexible than that of a snake, allowing the worm to stretch and change shape. In some types of animals the supporting structure encases the body and provides protection as well as support. In crabs and lobsters this exoskeleton, as it is called, is very strong and rigid. Smaller animals like insects also have exoskeletons but, because the animals are lighter, the structure is lighter too.

Humans are among the animals that have an internal skeleton made up of the tissue known as bones. Our skeleton is jointed, and large muscles are attached to the bones with tendons near the joints. This allows us to bend our limbs.

Larger animals need a strong rigid supporting structure either inside or outside the body, but this must not interfere with their ability to move.

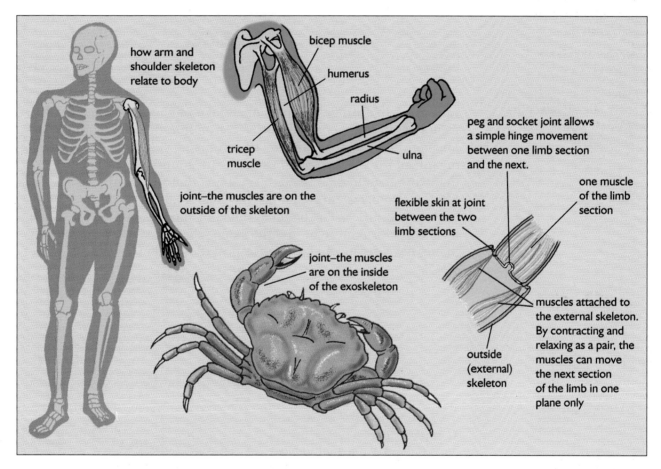

how arm and shoulder skeleton relate to body

bicep muscle

humerus

radius

tricep muscle

ulna

joint–the muscles are on the outside of the skeleton

joint–the muscles are on the inside of the exoskeleton

peg and socket joint allows a simple hinge movement between one limb section and the next.

flexible skin at joint between the two limb sections

one muscle of the limb section

outside (external) skeleton

muscles attached to the external skeleton. By contracting and relaxing as a pair, the muscles can move the next section of the limb in one plane only

Plant movement and support

Plants move more slowly than animals. They do not have muscles, nerves or a brain. The cells in a plant do communicate with one another, however, and they detect and respond to environmental stimuli. Much plant movement is accomplished by simply growing. The stem and leaves grow upwards to the light and the roots grow downwards into the soil. (See page 7.)

The structure of a plant is provided by strong flexible plant fibres made largely of cellulose. In many cases, the rigidity of plant tissues is due to the presence of water in the tissues. That is why plants wilt and go floppy when they need water.

6 Humans

Why does your heart rate increase when you exercise?

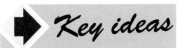 **Key ideas**

The human body is made up of organs and organ systems that have specific functions and interact with each other.

Human beings are mammals.

Many factors, such as diet and exercise, affect the health of our bodies.

Like all living things, humans must take in energy and materials from the environment and release waste into the environment. In large multi-cellular organisms like humans, specialized cells are organized into organs, such as the heart, lungs, kidneys and liver, that work together to create the systems that service the body. Similar organ systems exist in other mammals as well as in fish, birds and reptiles. The organ systems in smaller animals, such as insects perform more or less the same job, and all but the smallest plants have organized systems to provide for their needs.

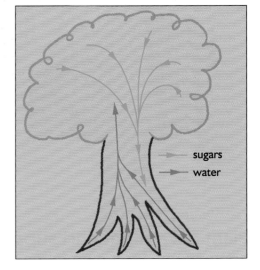

Most plants have a system of pipes that carry water, nutrients and sugar between the plant's stem and roots, but they do not have a means of rapidly pumping material around the plant.

The heart and circulation

The main job of transporting materials around the body is done by the circulatory system. Within the human body there are literally hundreds of miles of flexible branching tubes forming a network that extends to every bit of the body. The centre of this network is a pump, the heart, which pumps a complex liquid called blood around the network. The food, oxygen, wastes and other chemicals that need to be transported are carried around in the blood.

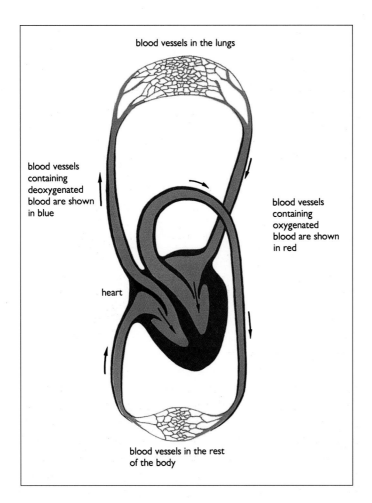

blood vessels in the lungs

blood vessels
containing
deoxygenated
blood are shown
in blue

blood vessels
containing
oxygenated
blood are shown
in red

heart

blood vessels in the rest
of the body

*The heart/lung
circulation
system*

A great deal of the ill-health suffered by people in later life is due
to diseases that reduce the efficiency of the circulatory system. In
many cases, the onset of these diseases can be delayed if people
keep their weight down, exercise, and eat a diet that is richer in
grains and vegetables than in foods of animal origins.

The human heart is divided to make two pumps, one on the left
and one on the right. Blood travels into a chamber on the right side
of the heart and then drops through a valve to the right pumping
chamber. The heart muscle then contracts, squeezing the blood
into a tube leading to the lungs where it picks up oxygen and
dumps carbon dioxide. Valves prevent the backflow of blood.

The blood then flows back to the heart, entering the left-hand side
this time. It drops down to the left pumping chamber and is
pumped out to the body.

Blood travels to the body along tubes called arteries, which branch
and branch forming much smaller tubes and finally becoming a
web of microscopically small tubes called capillaries. There are
capillaries in all the body tissues. As blood flows through the
capillaries, food, oxygen and other useful chemicals pass through
the walls of the capillaries and into the tissues. At the same time
the waste materials pass the other way into the blood. Then the
blood flows away from the tissues along tubes called veins, which
converge to form bigger and bigger veins and finally carry the
blood back to the heart.

*Children's
ideas*

Only a minority of children
seem to be aware of the
circulation of the blood
or the functions of the
heart and blood.

The air we breathe in consists of about 21% oxygen, 78% nitrogen and 1% water vapour and carbon dioxide.

The air we breathe out consists of about 15% oxygen, 75% nitrogen and 10% water vapour carbon dioxide and other substances the body needs to get rid of.

The lungs and breathing

When we breathe we draw air into our lungs. The air travels down a tube in our throat. This tube branches again and again as it goes down into the lungs and finally ends in a collection of tiny moist air sacs. Because of these air sacs, lung tissue looks and feels spongy. With each breath in, fresh oxygen-rich air is drawn into the sacs and oxygen dissolves in the layer of moisture lining the sacs. Each air sac is surrounded by a network of capillaries through which blood is continuously flowing. As the blood travels through, carbon dioxide is dropped off and oxygen is picked up.

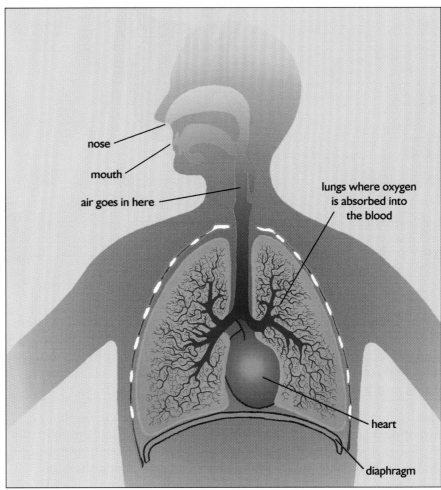

nose

mouth

air goes in here

lungs where oxygen is absorbed into the blood

heart

diaphragm

Exercising causes the breathing rate to increase because the muscle cells must respire more rapidly, breaking down more food in order to get the energy they need. Oxygen is used up and carbon dioxide created as the cells break down food. We must breathe more rapidly to bring in the extra oxygen and get rid of the extra carbon dioxide. The heart rate also speeds up to carry the extra oxygen and carbon dioxide around.

Fish use the oxygen dissolved in water. They keep a constant flow of water going in through their mouths and out through their gills. As the water passes through the gills oxygen is absorbed.

What do you think happens to food and drink in your body?

Food substances fall into six basic groups: protein, fat, carbohydrates (sugar and starch), vitamins, minerals and fibre. Often the packaging of food products shows how much of each group the food contains.

Digestion

The food we eat contains a wide variety of very complicated food chemicals that must be broken down into simpler chemicals before they can be absorbed by the body.

Beginning in the mouth where the food is chewed up and mixed with saliva, our food is turned into a watery mush. Saliva contains a digestive enzyme that triggers the breakdown of starch into sugar.

Food passes down the gullet to the stomach.

Food is stored and processed in the stomach and then passes into the small intestine.

Many other enzymes are added to the food as it passes through the stomach and the small intestine. Enzymes turn complicated food chemicals into simpler chemicals that can be absorbed by the body.

Cells lining the walls of the small intestine extract food chemicals from the watery mush. The food chemicals pass into the capillaries inside the intestine walls and are carried away in the blood.

Humans cannot digest the fibre that makes up much of the material of plants so no nutrients can be absorbed from it. This material passes on into the large intestine (or large bowel) where most of the water is removed. The leftovers are stored in the rectum and disposed of at a convenient time.

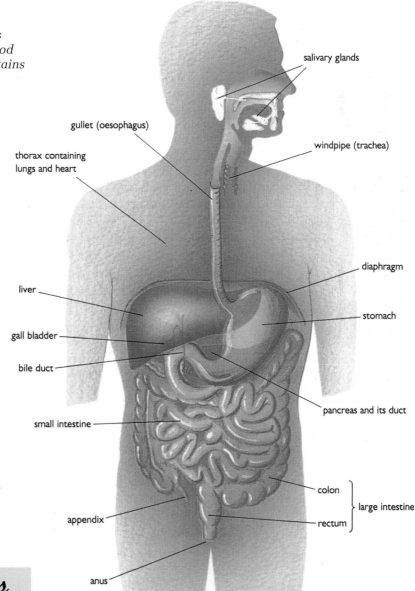

salivary glands

gullet (oesophagus)

windpipe (trachea)

thorax containing lungs and heart

diaphragm

liver

stomach

gall bladder

bile duct

pancreas and its duct

small intestine

colon

large intestine

appendix

rectum

anus

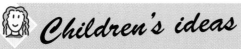

Children's ideas

Children often think that food and drink travel through the body separately.

Put your hand on your heart…your lungs, stomach, liver, kidneys. Where are they and what do they do?

Handling waste

Like all living organisms, the human body must have an effective way of handling wastes or our cells would not be able to operate. Humans have many ways of getting rid of wastes and other unwanted chemicals. When we exhale, we get rid of carbon dioxide and excess water and, if we have any alcohol in our blood, we get rid of some of that too. That is why we can smell the alcohol on the breath of someone who has been drinking. A number of chemicals are excreted via the lungs and the skin. When these are smelly, such as the chemical responsible for the smell of garlic, we can detect them on a person's breath and skin, unless we have been eating garlic too.

However, there are two organs in the body – the liver and the kidneys – that are particularly active in dealing with waste.

The liver

The position of the liver is shown in the diagram on page 21. The liver is equipped with chemical machinery that can break down a wide range of chemicals. It handles many of the chemical wastes produced in the body. It can also deal with almost all the strange chemicals, natural and synthetic, that we might accidentally or intentionally take on board, including of course alcohol.

One of the liver's trickiest waste-handling jobs is the disposal of material from old red blood cells. Red blood cells have a working life of only about three months, so almost one per cent of the body's red blood cells are disposed of every day. The haemoglobin in the cells contains iron, which needs to be conserved and used to make new red blood cells. The liver stores the iron and adds the rest of the materials in the red blood cells to the bile. This is released into the small intestine and leaves the body with the faeces.

The kidneys

The kidneys are at the back of the body, just above the waistline. (See the diagram on page 23.) They are the main organs of excretion. It is the job of the kidneys, working with the liver, to control the levels of chemicals in the blood so that all the cells of the body are bathed in a mixture containing just the right concentration of all the nutrients they need.

With every heartbeat about a quarter of the blood pumped out of the heart flows down the artery that leads to the kidneys. The kidneys do more than simply filter out waste chemicals from the blood. As blood flows through the kidney, its chemical balance is adjusted. Specific chemical wastes are removed, so is excess water and any normal blood chemicals that are present in too high a concentration. The water and chemicals taken out by the kidneys create what we know as urine. The urine from each kidney collects in a larger tube and trickles down into the bladder.

It is useful to think of the kidneys as being in charge of environmental control in the body. Of course, they do it more efficiently than any environmental service set up by humans.

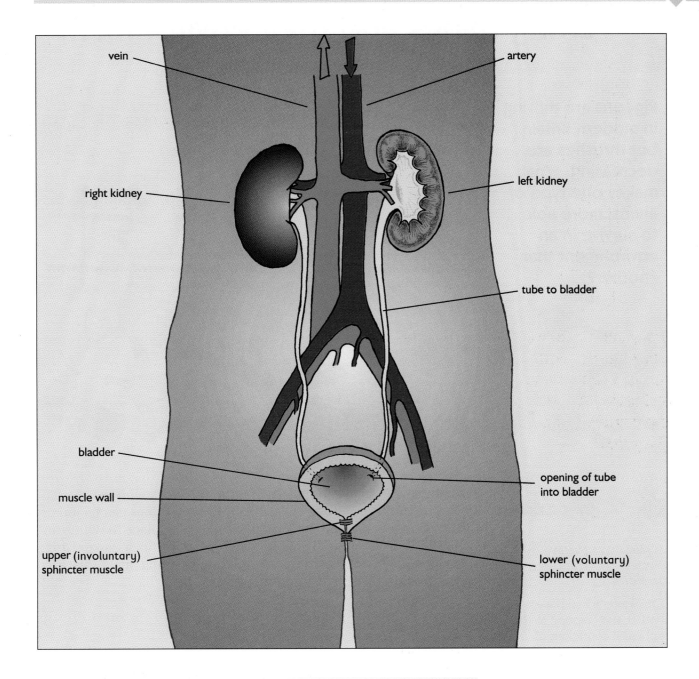

 Reflection

When it comes to handling waste, a living organism has exactly the same options as a town council:

✳ The waste can be turned into something harmless or useful.

✳ It can be placed somewhere it will not cause any harm.

✳ It can be dumped outside the town borders.

Living organisms use all these options.

The second is a more practical option for plants than for animals. For instance, tree trunks often contain waste products. But animals need to move around quickly and cannot be burdened by stored waste.

The third is seldom a safe way for a town to handle waste but is it often reasonable in the natural environment. One organism's waste is another organism's vital raw material.

Pigeons are thriving in modern Britain but thrushes are decreasing. What makes one type of animal more able to survive in an environment than another?

Key ideas

Living things live in a variety of places called habitats.

They interact with each other and respond to the physical conditions of their environment.

They are suited to the places in which they live.

From mountain peaks to the ocean floor, there is a wide range of environmental conditions on Earth, and living things can be found virtually everywhere on the Earth's surface. The place in which an organism lives is called its habitat, and the conditions that exist in its habitat make up the environment. A living thing 'makes its living' by exploiting its environment as

- a source of energy
- a source of raw materials
- a place to be
- a place that provides shelter
- somewhere to dump waste.

Of course the environment contains dangers too.

The living organisms that occupy a particular habitat are often referred to as a community. The word ecosystem is used when talking about the community of living organisms together with their habitat. Many components interact to create an ecosystem. They can be divided into two categories: physical conditions and other living things.

Physical conditions

Light, temperature, weather conditions, how much shelter is available and the chemical substances present define what a habitat or environment is like. These may vary over time, often in a cyclical way with the time of day or the seasons of the year. (See pages 28–9.) In some habitats the physical conditions vary a great deal. In others they are more stable.

Other living things

Living organisms interact with members of their own species and other species. All living things interact in three basic ways:

- they co-operate with each other
- they compete with each other (for food, shelter, space)
- one eats the other (predator and prey).

Members of the same species are likely to co-operate and compete with each other but they do not usually eat each other.

Living things can thrive in an environment only if they have characteristics that allow them to survive in the local conditions. Sheep can keep grazing even when the weather is cold, wet and windy. The hairs of their thick coats are covered with a waxy substance to make them waterproof. Birds' beaks vary a great deal depending on where they live and what they eat – see the pictures below of various types of beaks.

Falcon feeds on smaller birds and mammals, using its beak to tear the flesh

Curlew uses its long beak to find worms and other marine animals along the shore

NOT TO SCALE

Lark uses its beak to pick up seeds which it swallows whole

Puffin lives on fish and can hold several at once in its beak

Great tit lives mostly on insects which it catches with its strong beak

Plants that live in areas where there is plenty of moisture and not very much sunlight have many leaves. These increase the amount of light energy they can absorb. In the desert where the sunshine is bright and moisture scarce, leaves are often reduced to small spines, as on a cactus.

25

How do humans exploit their environment? How do they protect themselves from it?

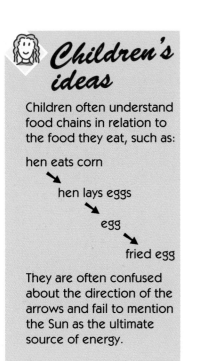

Children's ideas

Children often understand food chains in relation to the food they eat, such as:

hen eats corn

⟶ hen lays eggs

⟶ egg

⟶ fried egg

They are often confused about the direction of the arrows and fail to mention the Sun as the ultimate source of energy.

Humans share their environment with many other living things. Some plants and animals are our prey. We eat them. We co-operate with others – our pets, house plants and, of course, other humans. It is less obvious that human beings also have competitors and predators. The animals we call pests and the plants we call weeds compete with us. Insects like mosquitoes are our predators. Some of the most difficult living things we have to deal with are simple single-celled organisms like bacteria. Some of them compete with us for food. When they get to it first, they spoil it so we cannot eat it. Others are parasites. They live inside our bodies and sometimes make us ill.

Energy chains and food webs

There are two simple facts about living on Earth that apply to virtually all of the Earth's ecosystems:

- a supply of energy called sunlight is constantly being added to the Earth

- new supplies of material are NOT being added to the Earth.

An energy chain

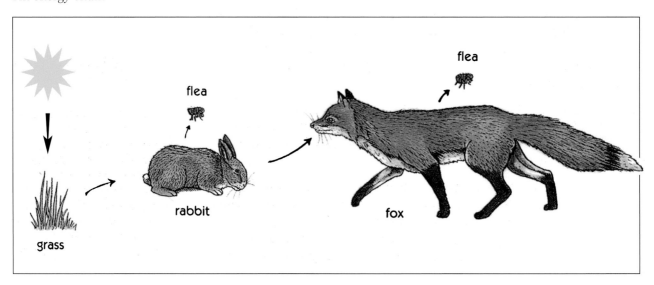

flea

flea

rabbit

fox

grass

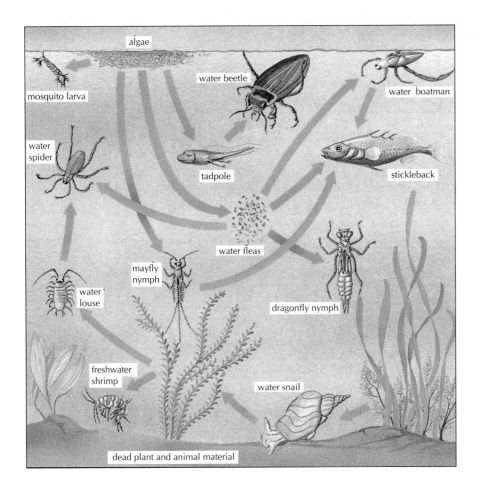

algae

water beetle

water boatman

mosquito larva

water spider

tadpole

stickleback

water fleas

mayfly nymph

water louse

dragonfly nymph

freshwater shrimp

water snail

dead plant and animal material

The feeding relationships between living things can be represented as food chains and food webs. This drawing shows a simple food web in a pond; the arrows show the direction of flow of energy and food.

This means that

- the *energy* living things need passes in one direction. It travels along a chain. (See also page 64.)

- the *raw materials* that living things get from the environment have to be recycled. They cycle around an ecosystem.

Decomposers

Many organisms make their living by consuming the waste released by other living things and by consuming their bodies once they have died. Many of these decomposers are single-celled organisms such as bacteria, but more complex organisms such as mushrooms and moulds (which are fungi) also live by decomposing dead material.

As they consume, the decomposers themselves produce waste chemicals but these are the very chemicals that plants must absorb in order to grow. Decomposers do the vital job of recycling the materials that living things need.

Like all living things, decomposers thrive only in the right conditions. They need a certain amount of moisture and they work more quickly when it is warm. We preserve our food and possessions by creating conditions in which decomposers cannot thrive. For instance, the fungus known as mildew grows only on damp materials.

Key ideas

Green plants are the ultimate source of food for virtually all living things.

The remains of living things will decay under suitable conditions. This releases the materials they contain, which can be taken in and used by other organisms.

Some materials change and decay quickly, while for others the changes occur over a long time.

Reflection

We only have our bodies on loan. Throughout the Earth's history the elements that make them up have been part of many other living things. It would be fair to say that everyone's body contains materials that were once part of a dinosaur's body.

Think of the wildest place you have ever been. How is it affected by human activity?

Children's ideas

Younger children, particularly those living in urban areas, may believe that nothing happens without a human cause. They may think that hills were made by people.

They may focus on the negative aspects of human influence, such as litter and vandalism, while nature is seen as attractive.

Environmental change and extinction

No environment remains perfectly constant, and living things are equipped to cope with a certain amount of change in their habitat. The plants and animals in Britain, for example, survive seasonal changes, most obviously summer and winter (see opposite). When an environment changes in new ways, however, living things find it more difficult to cope. The more finely tuned a species is to surviving in the conditions that previously existed, the harder it is for it to thrive in new conditions. If environmental change is too widespread and a species cannot find suitable resources to make a living, it will die out (become extinct).

Human activity

Although human activity is by no means the only cause of environmental change on Earth, in recent years we have profoundly affected the lives of other living things. It began tens of thousands of years ago when our hunting and gathering ancestors began to improve their hunting skills and technology. This coincided with the extinction of many large mammals including the mammoth.

With the development of agriculture about ten thousand years ago, the destruction of natural habitats began in earnest and, of course, in recent times this has increased at an alarming rate. An enormous amount of literature on environmental issues has been produced for children and for the general public. This book is not the place for detailed explanations and discussions of the problems. The fundamental story behind all the issues is that, over a relatively short span of time, humans have developed many new ways of exploiting the environment. As a result, we have been very successful in competing against other species for space and for the Earth's limited resources. We have discovered fossil fuels and nuclear fuels and this has given us extra supplies of fuels, but these supplies will not last indefinitely.

Seasonal changes

Like any successful living organism, we have reproduced at a very rapid rate and our increasing population means we exploit the Earth at an ever-increasing rate as we struggle to survive. At current rates of increase, the size of the human population will double every forty years. As we take up more and more of the Earth's space, we destroy habitats such as wetlands and rainforests that are the homes of huge numbers of other living things. As we exploit the materials in the environment more quickly, we also dump our waste into the environment more rapidly, and our invention of new ways of exploiting the environment has meant creating new kinds of waste.

There is every reason to believe that, in the future, things will get very much worse. The one hope lies in the fact that humans are capable of being aware of the problems we are creating. The very same properties of the human mind that allowed us to be so devastatingly successful in our exploitation of the environment may allow us to work together to prevent the devastation from getting out of hand. The rate of growth of the human population is now slowing. That is a first step.

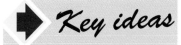

Key ideas

Many kinds of living things that existed in the past are now extinct.

Human activity has changed all parts of the environment.

The resources of the Earth are finite.

Materials can be re-used, recycled or discarded.

Many human activities produce waste materials that cause changes in the environment, locally and/or globally.

Which characteristics of living things are due to genes or to environmental influences, and which are influenced by both?

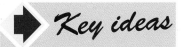 *Key ideas*

There is a wide variety of living things, which includes plants and animals.

Plants and animals, or parts of them, can be preserved as fossils.

Living things of the same kind vary from individual to individual.

Variation between individuals of the same kind results from differences in their genes and the influence of the environment.

Life forms have changed over very long periods of time.

The evolution of variety

Studies of the Earth and other planets have revealed that the Earth has existed for over four and a half thousand million years and there has probably been life on Earth for nearly four thousand million of those years. Under the right conditions, the material that makes up the remains of living things can gradually be replaced by minerals, allowing the remains to be preserved as rocks. These are fossils. Studies have revealed that over those millions of years, many different kinds of living things have existed for a while and then become extinct. Also, many of the plants and animals common today simply did not exist a few million years ago. Human-like creatures have existed for about three million years, but humans exactly like us probably only appeared about a hundred thousand years ago.

This is an observation in need of explanation because we know that each living thing produces offspring of its own kind. How then can new kinds of living things be born?

Darwin's theory of evolution provided a reasonable solution to the puzzle, and, as scientists gained a better understanding of how genetic information is passed from parents to their offspring, they became more and more convinced that this theory is correct.

To create offspring, a living organism must make a copy of its genetic information (see pages 14–15). This involves the copying of a lot of genetic information, and inevitably mistakes are made. Often the error makes no difference to the functioning of the offspring. Sometimes it garbles the instructions for making an important piece of cellular machinery and the offspring cannot survive.

Selective breeding has resulted in a great variety of dog breeds.

Occasionally, the mistake creates an offspring that functions perfectly well but has a component that is subtly different from that of its ancestors. It is these mistakes, called mutations, that cause there to be variation between different individuals within a species. It is thanks to mutations in times past that human beings possess such a variety of characteristics even though we are all fundamentally very similar.

Sexual reproduction creates offspring whose genetic information is made up of equal contributions from each of its parents. This ensures that each new generation has individuals with new combinations of inherited characteristics.

As breeders of plants and animals have shown many times, when there is a variation within a species it is possible to exaggerate the differences in future generations by selecting individuals with certain characteristics. For example, the vast variety of different dog breeds was created in the last few centuries by people choosing to mate dogs with certain characteristics – long hair, deep chest, a gentle temperament and so on.

 *Children's ideas*

Children are more likely to notice differences than similarities.

When asked to explain differences, young children in particular may simply say: 'God made them that way.'

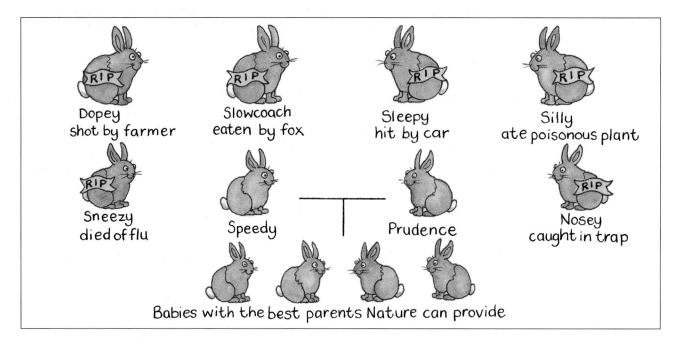

Dopey
shot by farmer

Slowcoach
eaten by fox

Sleepy
hit by car

Silly
ate poisonous plant

Sneezy
died of flu

Speedy

Prudence

Nosey
caught in trap

Babies with the best parents Nature can provide

Natural selection

Charles Darwin realized that nature selects breeding stock, in a sense like any human breeder. Living things routinely produce more young than can possibly survive. Only the ones that do survive grow up to produce their own offspring. In this way, natural selection ensures that the 'best genes' – the genes that carry the instructions for making the best survival equipment – are passed on to the next generation. Darwin also pointed out how new species could emerge from a single species: if populations of the same species are separated and isolated from one another and can no longer breed with one another, they change in different ways and could, after many generations, become two distinct species.

Earth's living things have changed over the millennia because the environments on Earth have changed. With each change, nature selected a different set of characteristics. Living things are not passive victims of environmental change. They are an integral part of the environment and their changes are often the most important cause of environmental change. For example, about thirty million years ago a plant arose that had the ability to grow very quickly and spread across vast tracts of land. This plant, which we call grass, was a new source of food for animals. Until then, there had been no grazing animals but the fossil record shows that within the next hundred thousand years or so, the ancestors of animals such as horses and sheep began to appear.

It is impossible to conduct an experiment that will tell us precisely how each species came about by evolution, but there are many ways of observing natural selection taking place in species that reproduce very quickly. For example, when antibiotics were first used to treat infections, bacteria resistant to antibiotics were rare so treatment seldom failed to bring a quick cure. However, the use of antibiotics selected these resistant bacteria by killing the others. The survivors reproduced rapidly and their offspring also thrived. Today doctors must often try several antibiotics before finding one that will cure an infection.

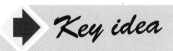

Key idea

Living things can be placed in groups according to their characteristics.

In order to get to grips with the bewildering complexity of life on Earth, science has had to sort living organisms into groups. It is possible to construct groups based on many different aspects of life. You can consider the following, for example:

- the ways they make their living (such as producers, consumers, decomposers)

- the environment in which they live (such as terrestrial, aquatic/marine)

- their economic importance (for providing, for example, food, building materials, drugs)

- their physical components (do they have, for example, fur or feathers, flowers or cones?)

- lifestyles (for example, do they live or grow with others of their kind or are they solitary?).

Biologists have recognized the need to create a fundamental system of classifying all life forms. Long before Darwin proposed his theory of evolution, naturalists had noticed that living things seemed to fall into families. Some basic characteristics were common to a group of organisms even though they had very different lifestyles. For example, dolphins live in the sea like fish and they are more or less fish-shaped, but in some very basic ways they are quite unlike fish and have more in common with dogs and humans, which are classed as mammals.

Reflection

Why a dolphin is a mammal:

✱ Dolphins have lungs not gills and must come to the surface of the water to breathe air.

✱ Their fins have a bone structure similar to that found in legs and are quite unlike the fins of fish.

✱ They are warm blooded. Unlike fish, they maintain a constant body temperature.

✱ The females have a womb and give birth to live young, which they provide with milk from glands similar to human breasts.

✱ Dolphins are not hairy but they do have a few bristly hairs. They do not have fishy scales.

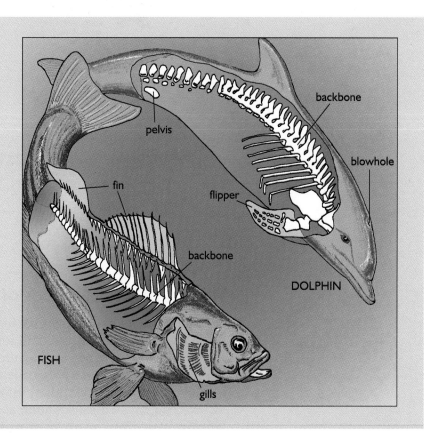

33

Children's ideas

Children have difficulty with the scientific grouping of living things, even into plants and animals. They tend to use these terms when describing particular plants or animals: flowers are plants but grass is not, a cat is an animal but a person is not.

In 1735, a Swedish naturalist named Carolus Linnaeus published a book called *Systema Naturae* that set out for the first time naturalists' ideas about the relationships between living things. In those days, when the knowledge of living things was limited, it seemed as though all life could be divided into two Kingdoms – the Plants and the Animals.

His classification system is still being revised. Below is a workable version: different scientists have different ideas.

Linnaeus's ideas about how scientists should go about naming and classifying living things are still followed.

Living things are still assigned systematic names. The same organisms may be given different common names in different parts of Britain and, of course, the world. (For example, see the list on page 35.) But their systematic names are based on Latin and are universal, so biologists in different countries can communicate information unambiguously.

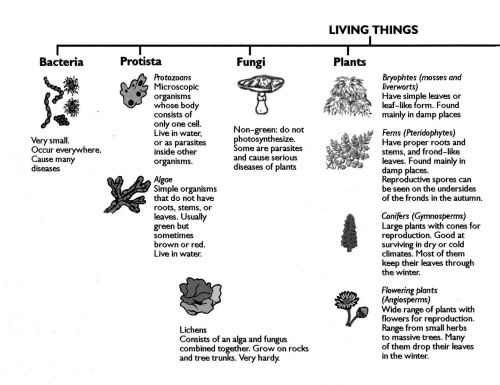

LIVING THINGS

Bacteria

Very small. Occur everywhere. Cause many diseases

Protista

Protozoans Microscopic organisms whose body consists of only one cell. Live in water, or as parasites inside other organisms.

Algae Simple organisms that do not have roots, stems, or leaves. Usually green but sometimes brown or red. Live in water.

Lichens Consists of an alga and fungus combined together. Grow on rocks and tree trunks. Very hardy.

Fungi

Non–green: do not photosynthesize. Some are parasites and cause serious diseases of plants

Plants

Bryophtes (mosses and liverworts) Have simple leaves or leaf–like form. Found mainly in damp places

Ferns (Pteridophytes) Have proper roots and stems, and frond–like leaves. Found mainly in damp places. Reproductive spores can be seen on the undersides of the fronds in the autumn.

Conifers (Gymnosperms) Large plants with cones for reproduction. Good at surviving in dry or cold climates. Most of them keep their leaves through the winter.

Flowering plants (Angiosperms) Wide range of plants with flowers for reproduction. Range from small herbs to massive trees. Many of them drop their leaves in the winter.

Viruses, only small pieces of life

Although the many forms of bacteria are extremely small, viruses are even smaller and simpler. Scientists do not always consider them to be living things as they are really just packages of genetic material. They invade living cells and are then able to multiply, killing the cell. They can then infect other cells. In humans, viruses can cause diseases such as HIV or influenza. They are not affected by antibiotics.

The systematic name also reflects the relationship between organisms. For example, donkeys, zebras and domestic horses are all members of the horse family. The Latin name for horse is *equus* so the systematic names for these animals are

- domestic horse *Equus caballus*
- mountain zebra *Equus zebra*
- donkey *Equus africanus*

To avoid confusion, systematic names are written in a certain way. The first name, known as the genus name, always starts with a capital letter; the second name, known as the species name, does not. In scientific literature the whole name is either written in italics or underlined.

Some common names for *Arum maculatum* (Lords and ladies)

Common name	Area where used
Cuckoo Pint	Sussex, E Anglia, Northants, Leics, Yorks
Fly-catcher	Wilts
Gentlemen-and-ladies	Oxfordshire
Parson's-and-clerk	Devon, Somerset
Toad's meat	Cornwall
Lady's keys	Kent
Small-dragon	Sussex
Kings-and-Queens	Somerset, Lincs, Durham
Ramps	Cumberland
Poison-fingers	Dorset
Hobble-gobbles	Kent
Dog-bobbins	Northants
Adder's-food	Somerset
Bobbins	Bucks

Animals

Animals without backbones
(invertebrates)

Coelenterates
Many–celled animals with tentacles and sting cells. Most of them live in the sea.
Example: sea anemone

Flatworms
Body elongated and flat. Some of them live in ponds and streams, but most are parasites causing diseases.

Roundworms
Body elongated and thread–like, round in cross–section. This group includes some harmful parasites.

Annelids
Body divided up by rings into a series of segments.
Example: earthworm.

Molluscs
Have a soft body usually protected by a shell. In some the shell is greatly reduced.

Echinoderms
Have a tough spiny skin. Most of them are star–shaped. They all live in the sea.

Arthropods
Have a hard cuticle and jointed limbs. Divided into four groups mainly on the basis of the number of legs.

Animals with backbones
(vertebrates)

Fishes
Live in water. Have gills for breathing, scales on their skin, and fins for movement.

Amphibians
Have moist skin without scales. Live on land but lay eggs in water. Have fish–like tadpole larvae which change into the adult.

Reptiles
Have dry waterproof skin with scales. Eggs have a leathery shell and are laid on land.

Birds
Have feathers. Eggs have hard shells. Wings for flying, and a beak for feeding.

Mammals
Have hair. The young develop inside the mother and after birth are fed on her milk.

Crustaceans
Live mainly in the sea, but some on land.
Examples: crab, woodlouse.

Myriapods
Very many legs; live on land.
Example: centipede

Arachnids
Spiders: 8 legs and 2 main body parts.

Insects
3 main body parts and 6 legs. Adults have wings.

35

Consider different ways in which you might group these objects. What criteria have you used for your groups?

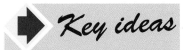

Key ideas

There is a wide variety of materials, both natural and synthetic, that differ in their properties.

Materials can be grouped according to their properties.

The uses of materials are related to their properties.

Children's ideas

Children use the word material to mean fabric.

They tend to classify objects according to their uses rather than their properties.

Making use of materials

Will this carrier bag break if I fill it with school books? Will this dish crack if I put it in the oven? Will these tiles wear away on the floor of a busy corridor? Will this mug shatter if I drop it? Will this branch crack if I swing on it? Will that window break if my football misses the net? There are lots of questions like these that you or your pupils may find yourself asking about materials.

The word 'material' is commonly used to mean 'fabric', the stuff clothes are made of, but it has a broader meaning and includes all the substances things are made from – metals, ceramics, plastics and wood, for example. In science, the word 'materials' includes the whole physical substance of the Universe, the earth we walk on, the air we breathe, the water we drink, the food we eat and our own bodies. This is how the word is used in this book.

A classroom provides many examples of the choice of materials available. We can use a clay plant pot or a plastic one, a woollen pullover or an acrylic one, a chair made of plastic and metal or one made entirely of wood. Many different materials can serve the same purpose; and a particular material can serve different purposes, for instance, glass is used to make windows and bottles.

Properties of materials

Grouping materials

There are many ways to group materials: by colour, by texture, by how they behave in water – do they dissolve...do they sink?

There are also certain standard groupings for materials, for instance, metals such as copper and steel, and plastics such as PET (chemically the same as polyester fibre), which is often used in soft-drink bottles, and PVC, which has a wide range of uses. These groupings are based on the properties and origins of materials, but the properties used to make the grouping are not always easily appreciated by children. For example, plastics have a wide range of properties. The metals children are familiar with are solid at room temperature, but mercury is a metal that is liquid at room temperature. Other metals melt if hot enough.

Properties and uses of materials

To make the best use of materials it is essential to know their properties so that we can choose the right material for the right job. We build bridges out of materials such as steel and concrete because these materials are known to have properties that make them able to carry heavy traffic loads for many years without breaking or changing shape. But in some circumstances it is important to use a material that changes shape easily. We don't make pillows out of concrete and steel; we make them out of materials that will allow the pillow to change shape as we move.

Some properties of a material can be judged by visual inspection alone. What colour is the material? Is it opaque, translucent, transparent or reflective? (see 'Reflections and shadows' on pages 80–1). Perhaps it shines with its own light like luminous paint. Other properties require investigation with other senses. Is the material soft or hard? Smooth or rough? Stiff or flexible? Does it smell? Sometimes the investigations involve doing things to the material, such as pressing on it, pulling it, or trying to break it, and measuring the effects.

Properties of metals

Most metals are solid, hard, strong, shiny, tough, dense. They feel cold. Some are magnetic.

Polythene is strong in a tough and flexible way. A polythene bottle does not crack but it does bend and can be permanently damaged by being torn.

Nylon is also strong and even more flexible. It will often bend easily but not break.

Glass is usually strong in a stiff and brittle way. A glass bottle cracks but is impossible to tear or bend.

Candle wax is weak in a stiff and brittle way. It will not bend and cracks very easily.

Jelly is even weaker. It is flexible but will also crack easily.

Steel is very strong and will support a heavy load. It bends without breaking.

Comparing solid materials

Property	Contrasting adjectives	Tests for the property
Strength	strong/weak	how much force is needed to break it?
Hardness	hard/soft	how much does it yield to pressure; how easily is it scratched?
Toughness	tough/brittle	how likely is it to crack?
Elasticity	elastic/inelastic	does it spring back after it has been bent, stretched or compressed?
Stiffness	stiff/flexible	how easily does it bend or stretch?

Comparing materials that are solid, liquid or a gas

Property	Contrasting adjectives	Tests for the property
Density	high/low density	how heavy/light is it for its size?
Thermal conductivity	thermal conductor/insulator	how well/badly does it conduct energy when hot at one end and cold at another?
Electrical conductivity	electrical conductor/insulator	how well/badly does it conduct electricity?

The effect of physical force

Testing the physical properties of materials shows that the same kind of force can cause different changes in different materials.

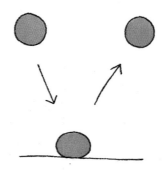

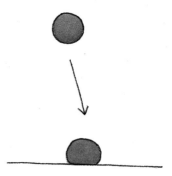

Pottery is brittle and breaks if dropped.

Rubber behaves differently from pottery because it is flexible and elastic. When it hits the floor, it changes shape briefly but then, as it bounces up again, returns to its original shape.

If you drop a piece of Plasticine, the shape changes on the side that hits the floor. The word 'plastic' is used to describe materials that do not recover their shape so easily.

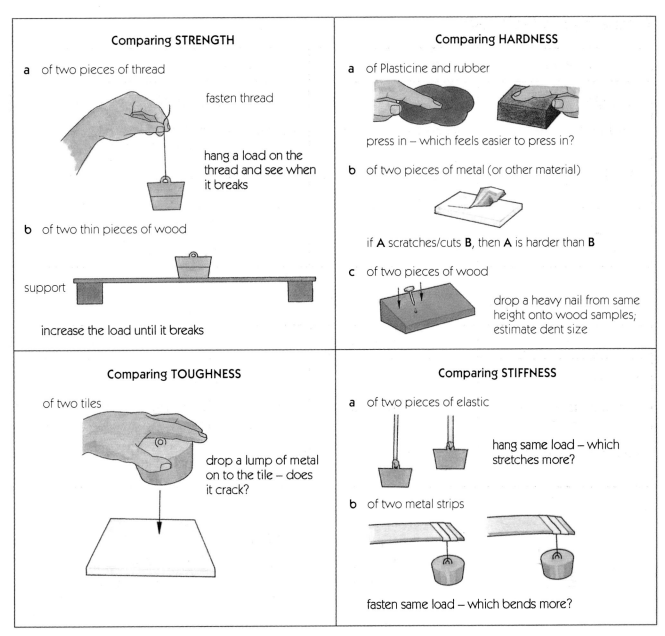

Comparing STRENGTH

a of two pieces of thread

fasten thread

hang a load on the thread and see when it breaks

b of two thin pieces of wood

support

increase the load until it breaks

Comparing HARDNESS

a of Plasticine and rubber

press in – which feels easier to press in?

b of two pieces of metal (or other material)

if **A** scratches/cuts **B**, then **A** is harder than **B**

c of two pieces of wood

drop a heavy nail from same height onto wood samples; estimate dent size

Comparing TOUGHNESS

of two tiles

drop a lump of metal on to the tile – does it crack?

Comparing STIFFNESS

a of two pieces of elastic

hang same load – which stretches more?

b of two metal strips

fasten same load – which bends more?

If you do these investigations in school, take care with heavy objects – put a container filled with waste materials underneath for them to fall into. Beware of threads snapping in children's faces.

Density

If we decide to pick up something that looks like a large boulder, we expect that this will take quite a lot of effort. If it turns out to be a prop from a Superman movie – a piece of expanded polystyrene shaped and painted to look like a boulder – we will be surprised and amused by its lightness. An expanded polystyrene boulder is lighter than a boulder made of rock because it is a material with a much lower density than that of stone. In other words, a certain volume of expanded polystyrene weighs much less than the same volume of rock.

Mass (the amount of stuff something is made of) and volume (the amount of space it takes up) can be measured, but these are properties of an object and are not unique to a particular material. The relationship between the mass and volume for any particular material is always the same – this is its density.

39

Solids, liquids and gases

Describe what is happening in this picture in terms of solids, liquids and gases.

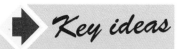
Materials can exist as solids, liquids or gases.

Heating can change solid to liquid and liquid to gas; these changes can be reversed by cooling.

Materials are made up of particles.

The differences between solids, liquids and gases can be explained in terms of the way in which particles are arranged.

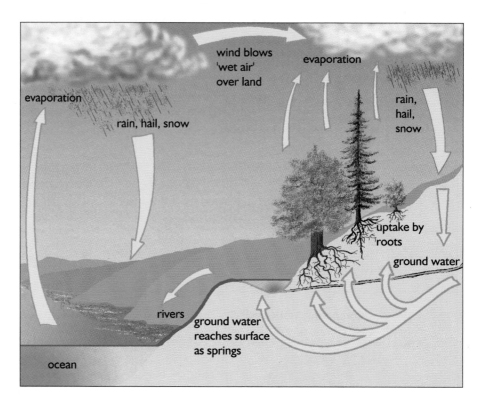

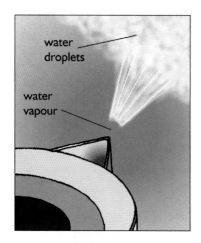

Boiling a kettle: liquid water to vapour to liquid droplets. Steam is really water vapour you cannot see; however, the word is often used for the cloud of droplets you can see.

Many substances exist in three phases, or states, depending on their temperature. For example, when its temperature is lower than 0°C, water is usually a solid, the stuff we call ice. If we warm ice up, it 'changes state' at about 0°C and becomes a liquid, the stuff we call water. If we keep making the water hotter and hotter, it boils. The water is changing state again. The big bubbles contain a gas, the gaseous form of water known as water vapour.

You cannot see water vapour, but it often condenses again in cold air and forms tiny water droplets that are visible as a white cloud.

Water boils (turns rapidly to a gas) as it reaches 100°C because at normal atmospheric pressure water that is more than 100°C can exist only as a gas. But water changes state between a liquid and a gas at temperatures much lower than 100°C, through evaporation.

Children often confuse the processes of boiling and evaporation, so it is helpful to distinguish between them.

Boiling	Evaporation
• takes place at a fixed temperature	• occurs at a wide range of temperatures
• agitates the liquid state	• no obvious agitation

Water is the one of the few materials that exists as a solid, liquid and gas in the narrow range of temperature naturally found on the surface of the Earth. Many of the liquids children are most familiar with, milk or soft drinks for example, are a mixture of water and other substances. They boil and freeze much like water but it is the water they contain that is really changing phase.

There are other liquids containing little or no water that behave quite differently in response to heating and cooling. For example, cooking oil has very different boiling and freezing points from those of water. The white spirit used to clean paint brushes boils at a lower temperature than water and will not freeze in the coldest domestic freezer.

Other substances around us are always a gas in normal conditions, for instance, the oxygen and nitrogen that make up most of the Earth's atmosphere, and methane, the gas we use as a fuel. If these gases are pressurized or cooled to very low temperatures, they will change into a liquid. At even lower temperatures, the liquids will freeze. Hospitals have regular deliveries of liquid nitrogen and other gases to cool the magnets in equipment used in modern diagnosis.

Reflection

Some changes are reversible. Heat ice and it melts. Cool the water and it freezes, turning back into ice. Similarly evaporating and condensing are reversible. The change goes one way or the other depending on the conditions.

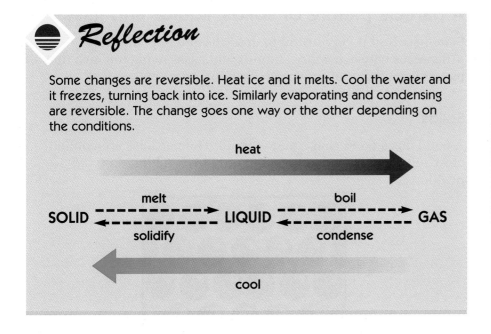

Children's ideas

Young children often do not realize that water can exist as ice and change back to water. They may think that ice formed on a pond in winter has been added in the way that we add ice to drinks.

Words and meanings

'Solid' is a word with many meanings in everyday conversation and a very specific meaning when used to describe a material. A solid material is one that has a definite shape and will not change its shape unless a force acts on it. A material that is 'liquid' has no fixed shape. When a liquid is poured into a container, it takes the shape of the container. It seems as if it should be simple enough to tell the difference between a solid and a liquid; and in the case of ice and water, it is simple. Once an ice lolly is frozen, it keeps its shape until it melts. But the distinction between liquids and solids is not so obvious in other materials.

Some liquids are so thick that they seem solid. Toffee, for example, is a very viscous liquid. The more viscous a liquid is, the longer it takes to assume the shape of its container. Heating up a liquid makes it less viscous, so it may seem as though the liquid is melting and freezing when it is really only becoming more or less viscous. When toffee is warm it obviously does pour, but as it cools, it gets more and more viscous. We talk about the toffee 'solidifying' but it does not become a solid.

Children's ideas

Children often use the word 'solid' to mean heavy, not flexible, or in one big piece. It is then difficult for them to classify substances such as flour or salt as solid.

Smoke is not a gas. It is made up of fine specks of soot and ash being carried upwards by the warm air rising from a fire.

We can see flames because, within the hot rising gases, a chemical reaction is taking place. This reaction gives out light (see page 48).

Reflection

The word 'particle' has more than one meaning. Sometimes in science books the word is used in its everyday sense to mean a small speck, such as a speck of dust.
At other times, as in this section, 'particle' is a general term for atoms and molecules, which are very much smaller.

What about talcum powder and sand? They seem to pour like a liquid and take the shape of a container. They are solids because, even though a whole mass of tiny grains of talc or sand does not have a definite shape, each individual grain does.

Most gases are colourless and therefore invisible, so you may have to work hard to convince children that they really exist. One way is to point out the visible effect of moving gases. Wind is moving air and air is a mixture of gases. Seeing things being blown along is reasonably convincing evidence that something invisible is pushing them. We can feel the wind pressing on us. Air is also responsible for balloons getting larger as we blow them up and for the bubbles that appear in a liquid when we blow into it with a straw.

A particle picture of solids, liquids and gases

Scientists find it very useful to describe and explain the differences between solids, liquids and gases using the idea that all matter is made up of tiny particles (atoms and molecules).

Solids

A solid has a fixed shape and volume. The particles are bonded close together. They do move, but only by wobbling in fixed positions.

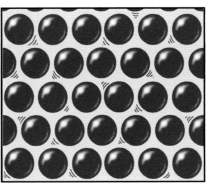
solid

Warming a solid makes it expand. As the particles wobble faster they move further apart. Some solids will melt. A solid like this changes to a liquid when it reaches a temperature that causes the particles to wobble so fast that they break free of their bonds and begin to flow.

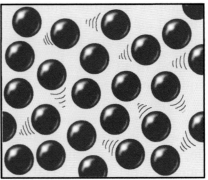
liquid

Liquids

Liquids change shape to fit the container they are in. They keep the same volume when you pour them from one container to another. The particles are bonded close together, but they can move round each other.

Warming a liquid makes it less viscous because it allows the particles to move around each other more easily. A liquid evaporates (turns to a gas) when the particles move so quickly that they break free of their bonds and escape from the surface of the liquid.

Most substances contract when they change from liquid to solid. Water is an exception – it expands when it freezes. This is why ice floats on the surface of water (see 'Density' on page 39).

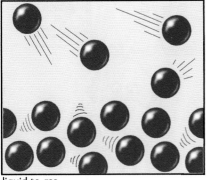

liquid to gas

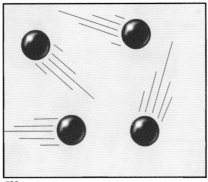

gas

Gases

Gases have no fixed shape or volume – they spread out to fill any container, and if you take the top off they will spread outside it. They are easy to squeeze into a smaller space. The particles are well spread out with nothing between them, and they move fast in all directions.

Warming a gas makes its particles move faster and further apart, causing the particles to press harder on the sides of the container.

A balloon will grow larger if it is brought into a warm house from the cold. The air inside expands and presses harder on the balloon. If it gets too warm it will burst.

Reflection

Atoms and molecules are so small that we cannot possibly see them. We have theories about what they are like and how they behave, and use chemical models to give us a picture of our theories. So you could say that these pictures show models of models!

12 Mixing and separating

What is in these mixtures?
Why are they useful?
Which are solutions and which are suspensions?

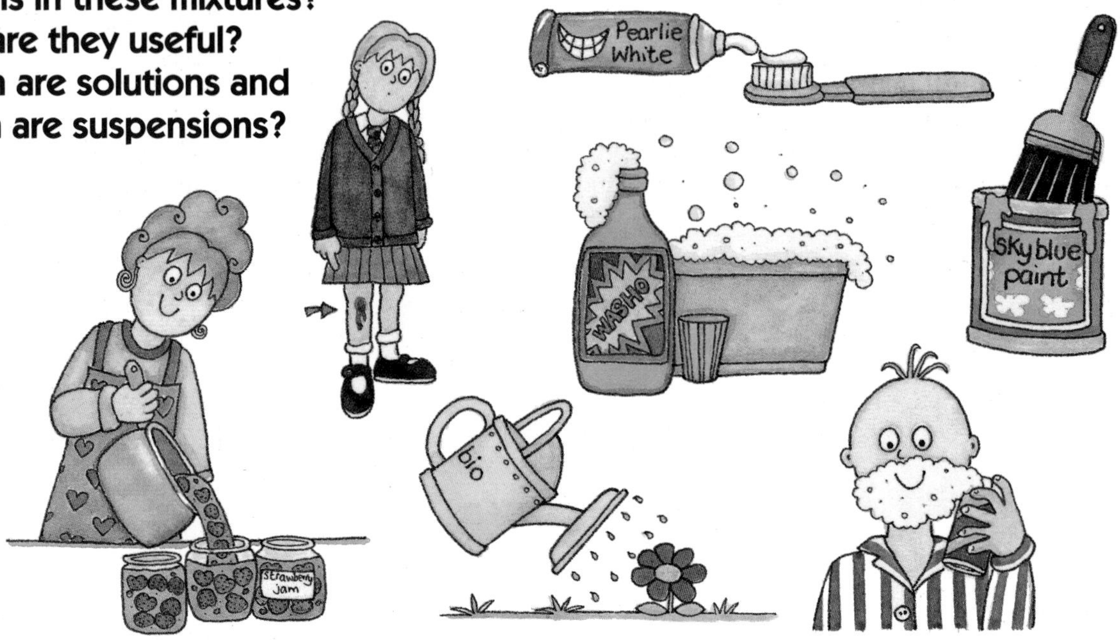

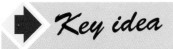

Key idea

Some materials occur naturally but may be purified or processed before use.

Mixtures matter in our lives. The industries that sell us everyday products employ experts to design the mixtures we need. They mix up ingredients to make ice cream and ketchup, paints and polishes, detergents, medicines and the other domestic products we expect to be able to buy. There are many natural mixtures too. Soil is a mixture of chips of rock, humus and living things. The sea is a solution of salts in water, while air is a mixture of gases, including oxygen and nitrogen.

Mixtures coarse and fine

Sometimes it is easy to spot a mixture. When someone has used the same teaspoon for instant coffee and then for the sugar, you can see the specks of coffee powder mixed up with the sugar grains. Similarly the lumps of fruit are obviously mixed up with the sugar solution in a pot of jam, and shaving foam is clearly a lot of little air bubbles surrounded by soapy water.

There are other mixtures where it is more difficult to see the different parts even though they are in fact physically separate. Paint is an example. There are very fine specks of solid pigment grains suspended in a liquid; it is a suspension.

River water is a natural suspension. Fine grains of rock or clay are carried along in the flowing water. The coarser grains settle where the water flows more slowly. Finer particles clump together and sink producing silt and mud where the river flows into the salty sea.

The salt dissolved in the sea is much more thoroughly mixed up with water than clay in river water. Dissolving is the most intimate way of mixing two materials together.

Dissolving

If you put a spoonful of sugar in some water it seems to disappear and you are left with what looks like water, but it is no longer tasteless. The sugar has spread completely throughout the water to create a sweet-tasting liquid. In other words, the sugar (the solute) has dissolved in the water (the solvent), forming a solution.

When something dissolves in water it mixes perfectly with the water, and the resulting solution should be transparent, though it may be coloured. When a tea bag is placed in hot water, some of the chemicals in the tea leaves dissolve in the water.

It is not only solids that dissolve in water. Liquids such as alcohol and many gases also dissolve in water. Water contains dissolved oxygen, which allows fish and creatures that need oxygen to live in water.

There are other substances that appear not to dissolve in water at all – sand and oil, for example. Sugar is said to dissolve well in water because a large amount of sugar will dissolve in a small amount of water. There is a limit to the amount of sugar that will dissolve in a cup of tea, but the hotter the tea, the more sugar that will dissolve.

Water is not the only liquid in which substances dissolve. Dry-cleaners wash clothes by soaking them in another liquid called perchlorethylene. Grease dissolves in this liquid leaving the clothes cleaner. A substance may dissolve in one liquid but not in another. For example, a smear of oil-based paint may not come off with water but will dissolve in turpentine. Salt dissolves in water but not in petrol.

People commonly think of dissolving as something that happens only in liquids, but similar kinds of perfect mixing can occur with substances in other states. In the air around us, for example, oxygen, nitrogen and carbon dioxide mix perfectly. It is physically difficult for two solids to mix but they can be mixed when one or both is in their liquid state. Bronze is made by mixing a little molten tin with some molten copper. The resulting mix of metals (called an alloy) has different properties from those of either copper or tin.

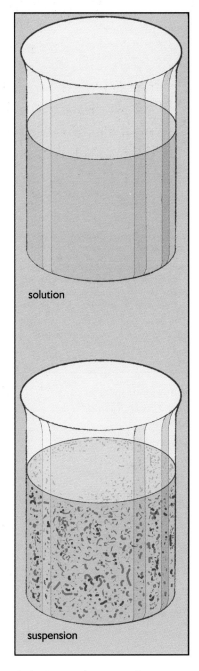

solution

suspension

Solution and suspension

Children's ideas

Children often describe dissolving as disappearing and say that the salt or sugar has disappeared. They often confuse the terms 'dissolving' and 'melting'.

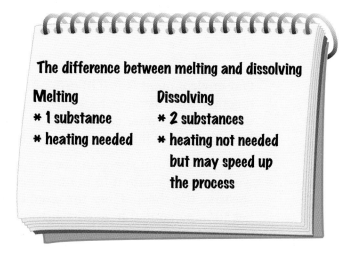

The difference between melting and dissolving

Melting	Dissolving
* 1 substance	* 2 substances
* heating needed	* heating not needed but may speed up the process

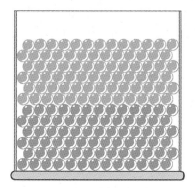

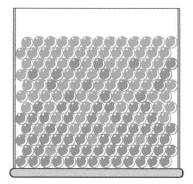

A model of mixing particles to form a solution

A particle picture of dissolving

When a solid dissolves in a liquid, we imagine that all the particles are very thoroughly mixed. Mixing up the atoms or molecules so thoroughly means that liquids are the same all the way through. Solutions are clear, not cloudy – unlike suspensions. In a suspension, the solid specks reflect and scatter light. In a solution, there is nothing to do this.

Separating materials

Knowing the properties of materials is not only useful in helping us select the right material in order to make things, it also provides us with a means of separating materials.

When you are faced with a group of materials mixed together and need to find a way of separating them, the properties of the materials provide a possible way of separating them out. For example, pieces of steel can be pulled out of a heap of rubble by running a huge magnet across the rubble. Steel, which is made of iron, will stick to the magnet. If you want to separate the sugar from sugar beet, you soak the crushed-up beets in warm water. The sugar dissolves in the water and beet pulp is left behind.

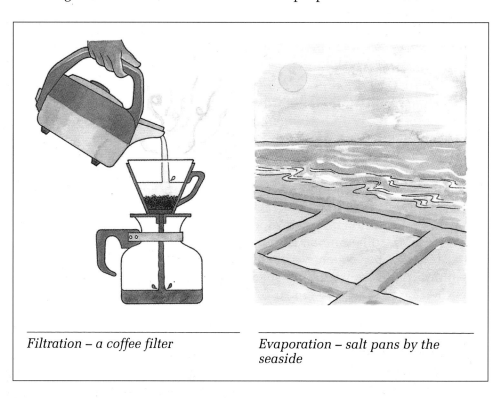

Filtration – a coffee filter

Evaporation – salt pans by the seaside

Our environment is full of different materials, often mixed together. For instance, rock may contain copper ore but in order to make useful copper metal, you have first to separate the copper ore from the rest of the material in the rock.

Wool comes from sheep but before we can make it into a jumper we have to separate it from other material. This doesn't just mean shearing the sheep. Once the wool is separated from the sheep, it has to be separated from dirt, bits of burdock and the waxy substance that coats the wool and makes it more waterproof.

How can you change ice? bread? sugar? aluminium? wood? flour?

Materials change: sometimes a material is valued because of the way it resists change and sometimes it is valued because of the way it changes.

The effect of heating

Different kinds of materials react differently to being made hotter.

Change from liquid to gas

Change from solid to liquid

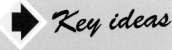

Harden due to change in chemical structure

Soften because cell structure breaks down (see page 11)

Chemical reaction with oxygen: burst into flame

The effect of other materials

When materials come into contact, they may do one of several things.

Mix but remain physically discrete

Interact so that one dissolves in the other

React chemically so as to produce one or more new substances (see pages 48–9)

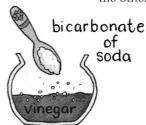

bicarbonate of soda

vinegar

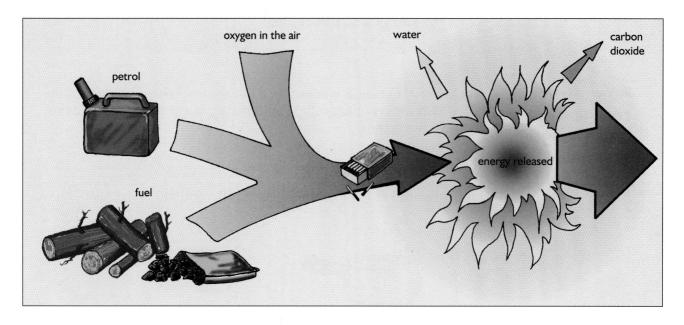

To explain burning we have to look inside the particles in solids, liquids and gases. Burning is a chemical reaction that does more drastic things to particles than just physically mixing them up. A chemical reaction tears the original particles apart and joins them together in a different way to make new particles, thus producing completely new chemicals.

Reflection

Temperature is a measure of how fast the particles are moving, but not of the total amount of energy in the substance.

A few particles moving very fast have a high temperature but only a little heat energy (for example, the particles in a spark from a flint).

Lots of particles moving relatively slowly have a low temperature but a lot of heat energy in total (for example, the water particles in a swimming pool).

Burning fuels

We value fuels because they give out lots of energy when they burn. We now depend on fuels to keep us warm, cook our food, allow us to travel and to manufacture all the products we buy.

Burning is one of the most common chemical reactions. Most fuels burn only when they are hot. We use a small flame from a lighter or an electric spark to get a bit of fuel hot enough to start burning. Once burning starts, it gives out enough energy to heat more fuel and keep the reaction going.

Fumes, smoke and ash

As a fuel burns, it reacts with oxygen in the air and makes new chemicals. The new chemicals are gases, so they seem to disappear into the air. When petrol or natural gas burn, the new chemicals are carbon dioxide and water vapour. On a cold day the water vapour in the waste gases from burning fuels condenses into a mist of water droplets, which make the exhaust fumes visible.

Wood is a mixture of carbon compounds, minerals and other chemicals. The minerals do not burn, so wood leaves an ash behind when it burns. When burning in a stove, however, there is often not enough oxygen from the air to make sure that all the carbon in the wood burns completely to carbon dioxide. This means that the burning wood is smoky and the specks of unburnt carbon settle as soot on the sides of the chimney.

Is burning reversible?

There is no easy way for us to turn carbon dioxide and water directly back into fuels. Burning is a one-way process; it is not reversible. Plants turn carbon dioxide and water into sugars by photosynthesis in sunlight (see page 12). Unfortunately there are not enough plants on land and in the sea to cope with all the carbon dioxide from burning coal, gas and oil, so the level of carbon dioxide in the air is rising.

Acids and alkalis

Not all chemical reactions need to be triggered by heat. Some just happen when two materials come in contact with one another. You can see such a reaction by adding a little bicarbonate of soda to some vinegar. As soon as the two substances touch, they react very rapidly. The reaction produces carbon dioxide gas and the bubbles of gas fizz up the vinegar. Vinegar is an acid. 'Bicarb' is an alkali.

Strong acids such as concentrated hydrochloric acid are very dangerous and must be handled with great care. But when diluted with water they are less of a hazard: dilute hydrochloric acid will not hurt your skin if washed away quickly, but it will sting in a cut and will slowly rot clothing. Not all acids are dangerous – many are part of life itself. They are found in living things: citric acid gives oranges and lemons their sharp flavour. Acetic acid is the main ingredient of vinegar.

Alkalis are just as much part of life as acids. Washing-up liquid and toothpaste both contain alkalis. Bleach contains alkalis. Farmers spread lime (an alkali) on their fields to help make sure that the soil is in a good condition to grow crops. Strong alkalis are more damaging to eyes and skin than acids.

When an acid solution and an alkaline solution are mixed together, they neutralize one another, making new chemicals.

The pH scale

Chemists use a pH scale as a way of measuring how strongly acid or alkaline a solution is. Very alkaline solutions have a pH approaching 14. Very acid solutions have a pH approaching 0. When a solution is neutral, its pH is 7.

Nowadays scientists sometimes use electronic instruments to measure precisely the pH of solutions; they also use dyes that indicate whether a solution is acidic or alkaline. There are several coloured chemicals found in plants that change colour according to the pH of the solution they are in. One of these is the chemical that gives red cabbage its red colour. You can extract this chemical, which in an acid solution is red and in an alkaline solution is blue. A coloured chemical that shows the pH of a solution is called an indicator.

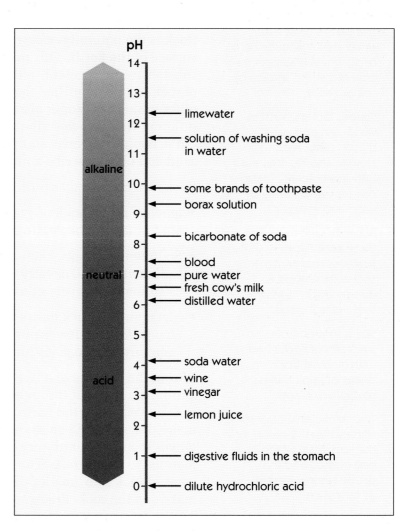

The pH scale

Where do rocks come from?

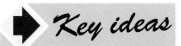

Key ideas

There is a wide variety of rocks and soils.

The Earth's crust – its outer shell – is made up of rock, which is sometimes covered at the surface by soil or water.

Various factors, such as wind, rain and living things, cause rock to change and disintegrate into small pieces. These can be carried away by wind and water.

Rocks belong to one of three basic types – igneous, sedimentary and metamorphic – depending on the way they were formed.

Soil is formed from very small bits of rock together with material from the decay of living things, particularly plants.

The characteristics of soil depend on the nature of the rock from which it was formed and the processes involved in its formation.

Rock

Walk about town and you will see many types of rock. Underfoot are flagstones, kerbstones and gravel. On walls are decorative examples of polished limestone and granite as well as building stones. On roofs you will see slate, sandstone slabs or clay tiles.

Rock is the naturally occurring solid material that makes up the surface of the Earth. This material is made up of a variety of substances put together in different ways, and the different kinds of rock can be identified from their colour, texture, hardness and other properties. Rocks also come in many sizes, and we use lots of different words to describe the sizes and shapes of rock. There are cliffs, boulders, stones and pebbles. Other words, such as gravel, sand and clay, describe a mass of small pieces of rock.

Rocks are classified according to how they are formed:

- Igneous rocks, such as granite, have large mineral crystals and are formed by the cooling of molten material.

- Sedimentary rocks, such as limestone and sandstone, form when sediments settle, usually under water, and become compressed as subsequent layers of material settle on top.

- Metamorphic rock has resulted from existing rock that has been changed by intense heat and/or pressure. For example, shale has been turned into slate, and limestone into marble.

Within the lifetime of a living organism, rocks undergo very little natural change; but throughout the four and a half thousand million years that the Earth has existed, the rocks have changed many times. The Earth's crust, which seems so solid, actually moves around as earthquakes and volcanoes bring new rocky material to the surface. The action of wind and water wears large areas of rock into smaller pieces and dissolves some material that makes up the rock. Freezing water expands and shatters rocks. The material produced is transported to new areas and the formation of new (sedimentary) rock begins again.

The uses of rock

Many rock types have the right properties to be useful building materials, and we have developed technologies that allow us to obtain many other materials from rock. Older building materials such as natural stone, slate and cobbles obviously come from rock, but so do the materials more commonly used today – bricks, mortar, concrete and plaster are all manufactured from different kinds of rock. Glass is made mostly from sand. Ceramic materials, from the porcelain and tiles in the toilets to the fine china in the tea service, are made from various types of clay.

Soil

A mixture of small pieces of rock becomes the stuff we call soil when living things begin to make it their home. It slowly changes as it becomes a complex community of many different kinds of living things – large organisms, such as plants, insects and worms, and, just as important, microscopic organisms, such as bacteria and fungi.

Soil also contains the remains of living things. The nutrients they contain are slowly being released as they decay (see page 27). Soil holds water and the minerals dissolved in the water. There are gases in the spaces between the solid and liquid material.

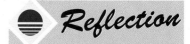

Reflection

The composition of soil is very different in different parts of the world, even in different parts of a single farm. These differences are due to the types of rocky material present in the soil and the kinds of organisms living in and on the soil. The composition of the soil influences the sorts of organisms that can thrive there – gardeners know that certain plants don't do well in certain kinds of soil.

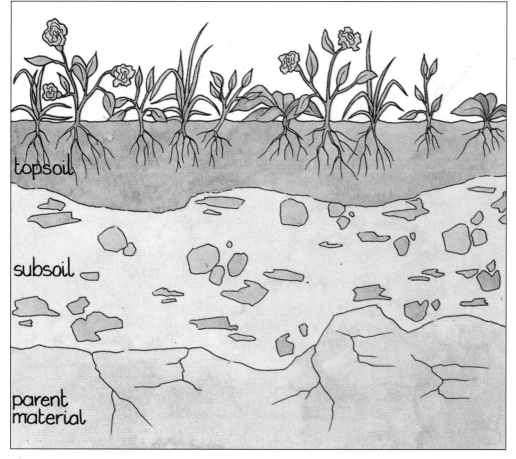

If you dig down deep enough in a garden in Britain you are likely to find the three layers shown in the picture.
* *Topsoil, which contains the decomposed remains of living things (mainly plants) mixed with finely divided rock material.*
* *Subsoil with larger and larger rock pieces and little or no plant material.*
* *Parent material, or bedrock, which is broken down to form the bulk of the soil.*

Why does the weather change?

We and all other living things rely on changes in the weather to provide us with fresh air and water. We have weather because some parts of the Earth's surface receive more of the Sun's energy than others and, because the Earth rotates around a tilted axis, the particular area of the surface receiving the most energy is continuously changing (see 'Seasonal change' on pages 90–91). This means the temperature is continuously changing. These temperature variations drive the movements of air and the process of evaporation that bring us our weather.

Differences in temperature

There is a big temperature difference between the air above the tropics and the air above the poles, but there is an even bigger temperature difference between the air that is close to the ground and the air that is higher up in the atmosphere. Most of the Sun's

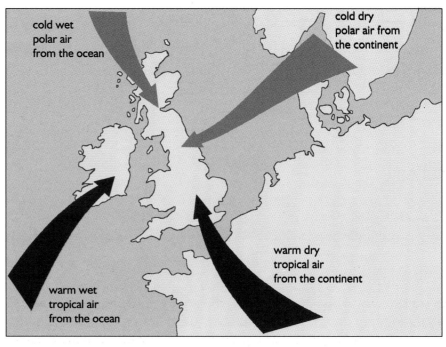

cold wet polar air from the ocean

cold dry polar air from the continent

warm dry tropical air from the continent

warm wet tropical air from the ocean

'Every wind has its weather.' Knowing where the wind is coming from gives people in Britain a good idea of what weather to expect.

energy shines through the atmosphere and warms the water and solid material of the Earth's surface. This in turn warms a thin layer of air just above the Earth's surface. As air warms, it expands. Its volume increases – it becomes lighter. It starts to rise, and cooler heavier air moves in to replace it. This is how the temperature difference creates a circulation of air around the Earth. Warm tropical air rises and is replaced by cooler air from nearer the poles. As the air rises, it cools and ultimately sinks once more.

Circulation of air and water

There is also a circulation of air higher up in the atmosphere (at about 10,000 metres) caused by the Earth's rotation. This is what is known as the 'jet stream', a wind that continually blows from west to east. Because of the jet stream, the conditions that create our weather usually move from west to east.

Water circulates because of the movement of air. The warming of the surface of the Earth causes water on the surface to evaporate and become part of the air. As the air rises and moves to a cooler place, the water cools and condenses to form drops of liquid water. If it cools further, it can freeze to ice. Within a few moments, water can go through its three different phases (see page 40).

When air moves, we feel it as wind. When air cools and the water it contains condenses to form tiny drops suspended in the air, we see mist or fog. If the mist is above our heads, we call it cloud. If a great deal of water condenses and the drops of water grow too large to be suspended in the air, they fall and we say it's raining. When frozen water falls out of the sky, we say it's hailing, sleeting or snowing, depending on what the ice is like.

Thunderstorms

On a hot sunny day, the air can become very warm and contain a lot of water vapour. When the air contains a lot of water, we say that the humidity is high. The presence of the water vapour means that sweat evaporates more slowly from our skin and we feel extra hot and sticky. Days like this often end in a thunderstorm.

What forces do you think are involved here?

Human beings are very good at moving things. We can kick a ball roughly where we want it to go, and if we practise we can vastly improve our aim. We can carry an awkward piece of furniture through a doorway and lift a delicate piece of pastry to our mouths. But what actually causes things to move?

It was Isaac Newton who first set his mind successfully to this puzzle. In 1687 he published a book in which he introduced a new way of thinking about forces and motion. A fundamental principle of Newton's explanation is that in order to make something move faster or more slowly one has to apply a force to it. Newton gave the term 'force' a very specific meaning; but in everyday speaking it can be used in many ways that are not always consistent with the scientific meaning.

We have many words to describe the different ways we apply force to objects. For example, we can push, pull, twist or squeeze an object.

A force can

- make stationary objects move
- make moving objects speed up
- make moving objects slow down
- make moving objects stop
- make moving objects change direction
- change the shape of objects.

Everyday forces and their effects

Children's ideas

Children may say that a moving object has an inbuilt ability to move. This is a good insight if it links to the idea that mass is a measure of how much force you need to speed it up or slow it down. It is unhelpful, however, if children think that a moving object has an inbuilt force that keeps it moving.

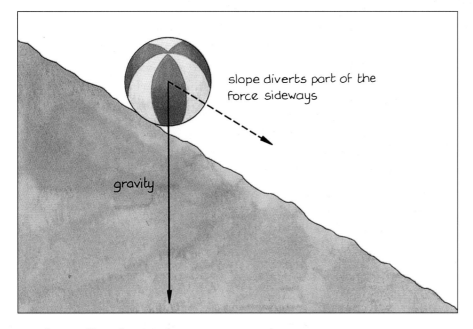

An object rolling down a slope

 *Key ideas*

Force is needed to change the movement of an object – to start it moving, speed it up, slow it down, stop it from moving or change its direction.

All things on Earth are pulled towards the centre of the Earth; it is a force called gravity that makes them fall.

Friction is a force that opposes the movement of one surface across another (or through a liquid or gas).

An object that is stationary or moving at a steady speed in a straight line is being acted on by balanced forces.

Newton said that the movement of an object will not change in speed or direction unless a force acts on it. The object will keep doing exactly the same thing, either staying still or moving along in a straight line. At first glance, Newton's idea seems silly.

If you roll a ball along the ground, it eventually stops. This is because of the force of friction between the ball and the ground – see the diagram below.

A ball thrown in the air falls back to the ground because of the force of gravity, which acts to pull objects towards the ground. You can read more about gravity on pages 86–7.

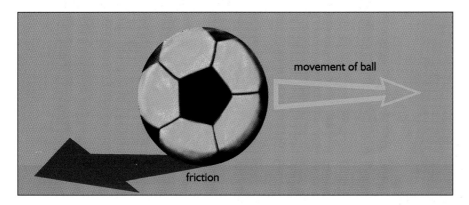

The friction is mainly between the ball and the ground, but there is also some friction between the ball and the air (air resistance).

 *Reflection*

If you throw a ball in the air, it doesn't just keep flying upwards; it comes down again, as shown in the picture on page 87.

What would happen if you threw a ball in Outer Space? On the Moon?

Friction

If you slide a penny across the surface of a table, it will slow down and come to rest. There does not seem to be any force involved in its slowing down, but there is. It is the force of friction that results from two surfaces moving against each other.

Some devices, such as brakes, use friction to work. The brakes of a bicycle press a pair of rubber blocks against the rims of the wheels. The harder they press, the closer each block gets to the surface of the rim and the greater the friction between the two surfaces. On a wet day our bicycle brakes are not as effective because water on the rim of the wheel acts as a lubricant and reduces friction.

The force of friction is stronger on some surfaces than others. The tread of a new tyre is said to 'grip' the rough surface of a road. The force of friction is much weaker on the very smooth surface of an icy road.

We rely on friction as we walk, so that our feet stay temporarily in place as our muscles move our body forwards. On ice, where the force of friction is very low, our feet can slide from underneath us.

Horizontal forces acting on our feet when we walk.

Your feet don't slip on the ground because the backward push from your leg muscles is balanced by friction force.

backward push — frictional force

We are most aware of the force of friction between two solid surfaces. But the tendency of substances to cling to one another when they are touching can be seen in liquids and gases as well. For example, as a boat travels through the water, it is slowed down by the drag of the water against the hull. This is the force of friction. A gas can cause friction too – a spacecraft coming back to Earth is slowed down a lot by our atmosphere and gets very hot because of friction.

Mass and weight

Newton's theories make a distinction between mass and weight, which often seems puzzling. Today we have the advantage of space flight to help get across the difference between these two ideas. Astronauts' masses do not change during a short space flight. But their weight can change, being greater on Earth and smaller on the Moon.

Weight is a force. It is the pull of gravity on an object. Like other forces, weight is measured in newtons. On Earth the pull of gravity is 10 newtons on each kilogram mass. So 1 newton is quite a small force, the pull of gravity on a 100-gram mass.

We get into difficulty when talking about mass and weight because we often do not measure masses directly. Instead we usually measure the pull of gravity and use this as a way of getting at the mass. So when you stand on a bathroom scale it responds to your weight, but the scale automatically converts the size of the pull into a mass because, on Earth, we can always say that the pull on each kilogram is ten newtons.

It takes a big kick to move a hockey ball along level ground; but it takes a smaller kick to move a tennis ball at the same speed as the hockey ball. Likewise, it takes more force to slow down or stop the hockey ball. We say that the mass of the hockey ball is greater than the mass of the tennis ball. On the Moon, you will find that the kicks you need to move these balls on level ground at the same speed as on Earth will be exactly the same as on Earth.

This idea of the mass of something, which is a measure of how much force you need to speed it up or slow it down, was part of Newton's explanation of motion. It is often called inertia. The inertial mass of a body does not depend on where you are (Earth, Moon, or anywhere else) even though its weight can change a lot.

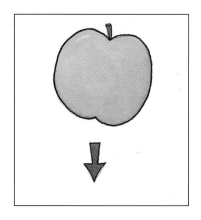

A typical apple has a mass of about 100 grams and weighs about 1 newton.

You can buy a bag of sugar with a mass of 1000 grams (1 kilogram) and this weighs 10 newtons.

Weight (the pull that gravity exerts on an object) is properly measured in newtons. You weigh less on the Moon than on the Earth, because the Moon has a smaller gravity pull than the Earth.

Mass, which depends on the amount of matter in an object, is measured in kilograms. Your mass is the same no matter where you are in the Universe.

Pressure and force

Pressure and force are often used interchangeably in everyday speech, but scientists use them to mean quite different things. 'Pressure' is a measure of how much force is being applied to a certain area.

Sometimes a force is spread out to give a low pressure. Camels' feet are large, so they spread the weight of the camel over a large area. This means that they do not sink into soft sand.

At other times a force is concentrated into a small area to give a high pressure. Sharks have sharp teeth. As a shark closes its jaws the teeth concentrate the force on a small area, giving an enormous pressure on the flesh of its prey. Drawing pins have sharp points. Pressing on a drawing pin gives a concentrated force that has enough pressure to push the point in. The head of the drawing pin has a much larger area, so the pressure on the finger is low.

Who has left marks on the floor?

What are the forces acting on the books?

Key idea

Stable/balanced objects are being acted on by balanced forces.

Balanced forces

Forces are often balanced during the tense, early phase of a tug-of-war when both teams are fresh and pulling on the rope with equal but opposite forces. The rope does not move until one team begins to tire; the other team is now the stronger and pulls away the rope to romp home to victory.

Underwater divers strap on a heavy belt to help them sink; later they blow gas into their suits to help them rise to the surface. They neither sink nor rise if they get the forces balanced, so that the downward pull of gravity is exactly equalled by the upthrust of the water.

Balanced forces cancel out, so we are often unaware of them. There generally seems no need to explain why a book on a table stays still. For most purposes we can ignore the fact that the book does not move because the downward pull of gravity is balanced by an upward push on the book by the table.

This upward push is harder to see, but if we look first at a book placed on foam rubber, we can see that the book squashes the rubber. We can also feel with our hands that, if we squash foam rubber, it pushes back on our hands. Indeed, if we squash anything – a spring or a car tyre – it pushes back on us; similarly if we stretch things, such as elastic bands, they pull back on us. The foam rubber pushes back on the book as it is squashed. The table top does exactly the same thing, but because it is made of much stronger material the squashing is too small for us to see.

If we stood an elephant on the table then we might see changes. However, the pressing back of the table top might not be enough to balance the weight of the elephant – the table would break and the elephant would fall through.

Children's ideas

Children think of forces in terms of movement, not staying still.

Children are likely to believe that if something is not moving there are no forces acting on it.

Nevertheless simple examples such as this can help us to appreciate that, on Earth, there are always forces acting on objects, particularly the force of gravity. A full understanding of forces and movement calls for an explanation of why things stay still as well as why they move.

Balanced forces are an abstract way of thinking about everyday situations when nothing much seems to be changing. A stationary object stays still if the forces acting on it are balanced. A moving object goes on moving at a steady speed in the same direction if the forces on it are balanced.

In all these examples the opposing forces are in a line. If the opposing forces are not in a line they may make the object twist or turn. Then we are into a different way that forces cancel each other out.

Reflection

A car travelling along the motorway at exactly 70 mph in a straight line is a situation in which the forces are balanced.

Turning forces

Children soon find out that a light child on a see-saw can balance a heavy one by sitting further way from the pivot. On a see-saw the weight of each child provides a turning force around the pivot. Here the two forces are not in line. They both point in the same direction but they have an opposite effect because of the pivot.

The turning effect of a force depends on both the size of the force and its distance from the pivot. When the force multiplied by the distance from the pivot is the same for each side of the see-saw, it will balance.

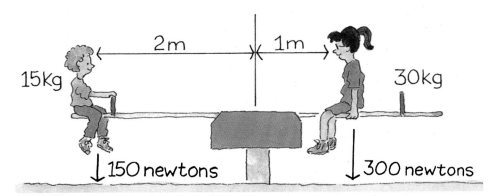

A light child balancing a heavy child on a see-saw

Children experience the effects of buoyancy whenever they go swimming. They can easily carry one another, or even an adult, as long as what they are carrying is under water. The effects of buoyancy are especially noticeable if you try to push inflated armbands under the water.

Floating and sinking: forces

If you hold a plastic ball under water you can feel the water pushing up on the ball. If you release the ball, it will shoot upwards. The upward push of the water is what we call upthrust. Upthrust is the force that makes things seem buoyant when in water.

So two forces decide whether or not an object will float or sink. Gravity pulls the object down. Upthrust pushes it up.

Floating and sinking in water

When something floats in water, the downward pull of gravity is equal to the upthrust of the water. The two forces balance and the object stays still.

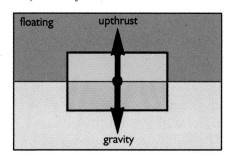
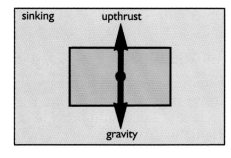

When something sinks, the downward pull of gravity is greater than the upthrust. This results in a force acting downwards, so the object moves downwards.

How big is the upthrust?

Floating

If you slowly lower a block of wood into some water you will feel the upthrust getting bigger as more water is displaced. The size of the upthrust is, in fact, equal to the weight of water displaced. The wood floats because it is able to displace its own weight of water before becoming completely submerged.

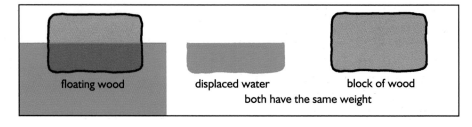

floating wood   displaced water   block of wood
both have the same weight

Sinking

If you do the same with a solid block of iron, the upthrust increases until the block is completely immersed, but the upthrust never gets as large as the weight of the block so the iron continues to sink.

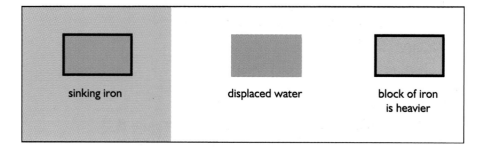

sinking iron

displaced water

block of iron is heavier

This is a general rule: if the object is lighter than the same volume of water, it will float. If it is heavier than the same volume of water, it will sink. This is the same as saying that objects that are less dense than water will float, and those that are more dense will sink (see page 39).

Oil floats on water because it is less dense than water. Somewhat surprisingly cream is less dense than milk (because of the fat content), so it floats on top of the milk. A cup of cream has less weight than a cup of milk.

A material that normally sinks can be made to float by forming it into a hollow shape, so that it displaces more water than a solid body of that amount of material would. Thus an iron ship will float. As the picture shows, most of the volume of the ship that is below the surface of the water is occupied not by iron but by air.

> **Reflection**
>
> A submarine, which is basically hollow, sinks by deliberately taking in some water so as to increase its weight. The force of gravity becomes greater than the upthrust and the boat moves downwards. It rises to the surface by blowing out the water. The force of gravity becomes less than the upthrust and the boat rises.

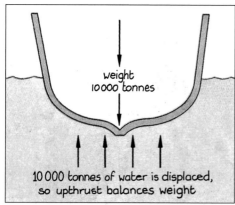

weight
10 000 tonnes

10 000 tonnes of water is displaced,
so upthrust balances weight

The forces on an iron ship

Floating in air

What has been said about liquids such as water applies to gases, such as air. An object will float in air if it can displace its own weight of air.

A balloon filled with helium gas is lighter than the same balloon filled with air, so it will float in air.

In fact, the weight of air displaced is greater than the weight of the helium-filled balloon. This means that the upthrust is greater than the weight and so the balloon rises.

Hot-air balloons rise because the heated air is lighter (less dense) than the surrounding air. The upthrust is bigger than the weight of the balloon. If the upthrust is big enough, it can support the weight of a basket and people as well as the weight of the balloon.

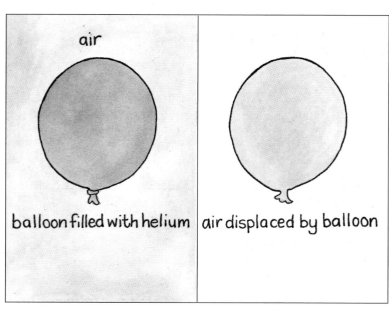

air

balloon filled with helium

air displaced by balloon

A ten-year-old child produced this drawing when asked to explain the working of a clockwork toy. Interestingly the child has used two ways of describing and explaining how the mechanism works. On the right the child has explained the works in terms of forces. On the left the child has suggested an explanation in terms of energy.

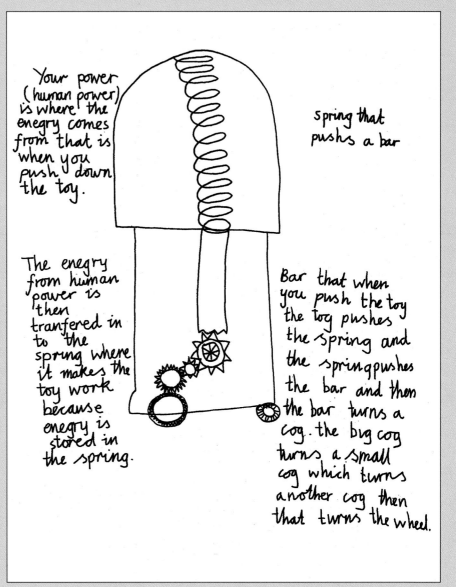

Your power (human power) is where the enegy comes from that is when you push down the toy.

The enegy from human power is then tranfered in to the spring where it makes the toy work because enegy is stored in the spring.

spring that pushs a bar

Bar that when you push the toy the toy pushes the spring and the springpushes the bar and then the bar turns a cog. the big cog turns a small cog which turns another cog then that turns the wheel.

Energy ideas in science

Ideas about energy run through all of science today. The idea crops up many times in this book. Here are some examples:

- Living cells need a supply of energy. They get energy in two main ways: from sunlight (the plant way) and from the energy released when the chemicals in food combine with oxygen (the animal way): pages 10–11.

- Fossil fuels (when combined with oxygen) and nuclear fuels give us extra supplies of energy, but these fuels will not last for ever: page 28.

- Some materials conduct energy more easily when hot at one end and cold at the other: page 38.

- We value fuels because they release energy when they burn: page 48.

- We have weather because some parts of the Earth's surface receive more of the Sun's energy than other parts: page 52.

- An electric current is a way of transferring energy: page 70.

- Echoes happen when the energy of the vibrations (in sound waves) is reflected off the surface of a second material: page 76.

- Light is like a stream of packets of energy: page 78.

So we use energy explanations to account for the growth of plants, the movement of animals, the heating effect of burning fuels, the effects of temperature differences, weather phenomena, sound and light, as well as the movement of machines and engines.

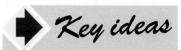

Key ideas

Force is needed to change the movement of an object – to start it moving, speed it up, slow it down, stop it from moving or change its direction. (See page 64 for the link between the two ideas: force and energy.)

Energy can be stored.

Energy is transferred, for example, by heating or by forces making things move.

Everyday energy ideas

Energy stories crop up regularly in the news because of the political, economic and environmental problems linked to the use of energy resources on a large scale. Unfortunately our thinking about energy can easily get confused because the meanings attached to the word in everyday conversation are often inconsistent with the scientific view.

Children often say things such as 'I have lots of energy so I can run about,' or 'I am worn out, I've no energy left.'

Such remarks suggest that energy is a substance that can be used up. This is not quite correct. Scientifically energy cannot be used up, but energy resources can – including foods such as fats and carbohydrates.

Acceptance of the scientific idea that energy is conserved is made difficult by everyday remarks such as 'We need to save energy.' If the amount of energy stays the same in all changes, then why do we need to save it and how can we use it up? In fact, what we usually mean is not energy but fuel. We do indeed have limited fuel resources and these can, in time, be exhausted.

An analogy

An analogy with money can help to clarify some aspects of the scientific concept of energy. We can store money in various ways: in bank accounts, in building society deposits or in a sock under the bed. Likewise we can store energy in a variety of ways: for example, by winding up a spring, by pumping water to the upper lake of a pump storage system, or by charging up a car battery.

Nothing much happens when money is just stored. Life gets interesting when we start giving our money to others to buy things or pay for services. We have a choice of ways of transferring money. We can pay with cash, write a cheque, use a credit card or just give instructions over a telephone or computer link.

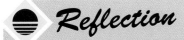

Reflection

Energy transfer happens in many ways. Here is one example.

bean growing

eaten by little girl

jumping on the mattress

bed springs compress then bounce back again

It is much the same with energy. Things happen when we transfer it. Forces transfer energy as they move things, as in the child's toy on page 62 where the forces in the mechanism transfer the energy stored in a coiled spring to the moving toy. Heating, lighting, sound and electricity are also ways of transferring energy from one place to another. Heating water in a saucepan transfers energy from the hot flame to the cooler water. Light carries energy from the Sun to plant leaves where photosynthesis converts simpler chemicals into sugars and oxygen. Electric currents bring energy from fuels burning in distant power stations to our homes to run appliances.

Above all, we can do calculations with money. Accountants have a central role in commerce and public life. They can work out how much we have earned, what we have spent, and what we can buy with the money we have left.

In science, energy is similarly important because it can be used for calculations that tell us what is possible and how far things can go. This applies to machines and engines, chemical processes and the growth of living things. Scientists are energy accountants following the laws that govern energy and change (these are the laws of thermodynamics).

Like all analogies the comparison between energy and money can break down. Politicians can 'print' money thereby increasing the amount of money circulating in the economy. There is no energy equivalent of inflation: energy cannot be created or destroyed.

Energy and change

An understanding of why things change is of fundamental importance to science. Energy is involved in so many changes that it is tempting to think that it is 'energy that makes things go'. This is such a common idea that it comes as a bit of a surprise to realize that energy is not the go of things. After all, if energy is conserved there is the same amount of energy before and after every change.

We can have a lot of energy but if it is evenly spread nothing can happen. To make a change we need a difference. We need a concentration of energy that can then spread out in some way. That is why fuels are so important: they supply concentrated energy at high temperatures when they burn. It is the spreading out and the disappearance of the difference that drives change.

A flame, for example, heats a pan of water, not because the flame has a lot of energy but because the flame is hotter: its energy is more concentrated than the energy in the water. Fuels are valuable, and should be conserved, because together with oxygen they are able to create the differences that allow us to make the changes we want, such as heating or driving engines.

Energy spreads out

The concentrated energy from a burning fuel in an engine spreads out into the surroundings. A well-designed engine can harness some but not all of the energy as it spreads out to drive a machine.

The energy goes from where it was concentrated to the broad surroundings. Overall no energy is lost but by being spread about it becomes useless.

In a car as little as ten per cent of the energy from the burning petrol is turned to useful movement. The rest is wasted as the exhaust gases and the hot engine and radiator heat up the surrounding air.

The energy that makes the car move also ends up heating the air and ground, thanks to the friction between tyres and the road, air resistance, sound and, finally, friction heating in the brakes.

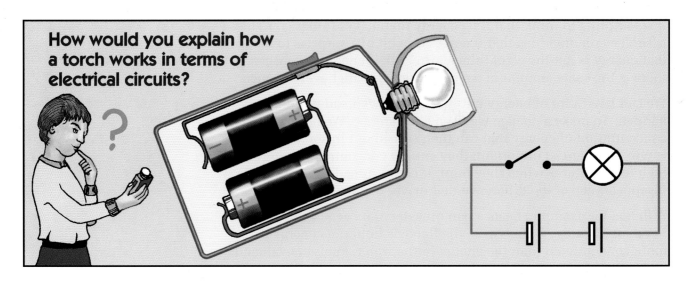

How would you explain how a torch works in terms of electrical circuits?

Simple circuits

The diagram below shows what goes on in a circuit with a light bulb connected by wires to a battery.

Batteries have two terminals. In a simple circuit, the current flows from one terminal through the wire and into the light bulb, out of the light bulb and along another wire to the second terminal. This is a complete circuit in which the current is flowing continuously in one direction (direct current, DC).

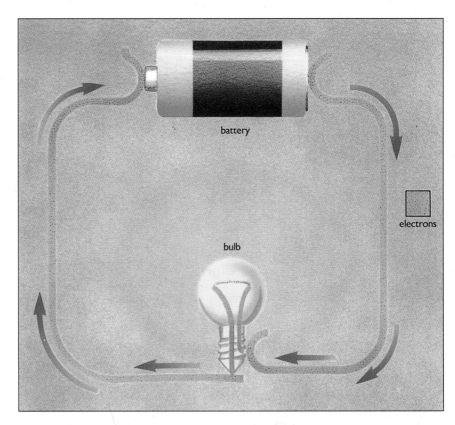

Flow of particles (electrons) in a circuit

Flow of electricity

An electrical current in a metal is a flow of negative charges called electrons. In the simple circuit a bulb can give a rough indication of the size of the current. The bigger the current the brighter the bulb.

Ordinary torch bulbs are quite variable so they are not reliable indicators of the size of the current. In theory two bulbs in a simple circuit (one after the other) should be equally bright because they have the same current flowing through them. In practice the bulbs are often not exactly the same – this is because their filaments are not identical.

Conductors and insulators

All materials offer some resistance to the flow of current. Metals have only slight resistance so they let the current through easily, which is why they are used to make the wires in circuits. Copper and aluminium are often used as electrical conductors because they are particularly good conductors for their price. Silver and gold are even better but they are used only in special cases because they are very expensive.

A current flows more easily through thick wires than thin wires. In other words, thinner wires have a higher resistance. In a simple circuit with a bulb, most of the resistance to the flow is due to the very thin wire of the filament.

Some materials offer a very high resistance, allowing almost no electrical current to flow through. These are non-conductors, or insulators. They include plastics, glass and rubber. The layer of plastic surrounding electric wiring makes sure that the electrical charges stay in the wires and do not travel through other conductors, including people.

Voltage

A typical torch battery is labelled '1.5 volts'. Voltage is a measure of the amount of energy given to the electrical charges that flow round the circuit.

Switches

A switch is a gap in a circuit that can be opened and closed. When the gap is open, the circuit is broken and no current flows. The working parts of switches are contacts – pieces of metal that move together or apart. A switch works wherever it is in the circuit.

Circuits

A short circuit is a route with a very low resistance compared with the rest of the circuit, so most of the current will pass that way.

When the current in a circuit with a motor changes direction, the motor changes direction too. This is because the magnetic field around the wire has changed direction. Some buzzers work only when they are connected to the battery in a particular direction.

Controlling the flow

The simplest way of varying the current in a circuit is to alter the resistance. A convenient material to use is graphite because it conducts electricity moderately well. You can use a graphite pencil 'lead' to vary the brightness of a small bulb. By sliding the wires together along the lead you reduce the resistance so the current increases and the bulb glows more brightly.

This principle can be used in the volume control of a radio, which has a metal arm sliding along a track of graphite. Dimmers used for room lighting, however, use electronic devices. These work in a completely different way but have the same effect.

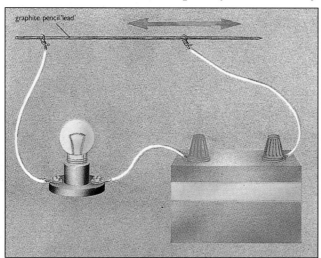

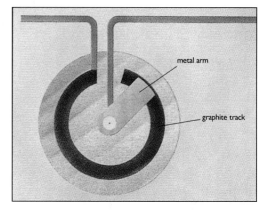

Volume control

Model dimmer

Series and parallel circuits

There are two ways of connecting up a circuit with two bulbs. If the bulbs are in a line they are in series. The current has to flow through both wires, so it has twice as far to go along the thin wire. The resistance of two bulbs in series is twice that of one bulb on its own. Doubling the resistance halves the current (if the battery stays the same). Both bulbs glow dimly but the battery lasts twice as long.

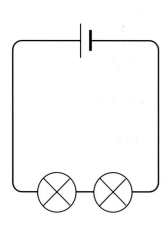

Bulbs (lamps) in series

If there is a branch in the circuit, the bulbs are side by side in parallel. The current flowing through the wires connected to the battery terminals now doubles because the current through each bulb is the same as if it were in the circuit alone. If the bulbs are identical and the battery new enough to supply double the current, then both bulbs should be equally bright – as bright as one bulb in the circuit on its own. (A single battery is also known as a cell.)

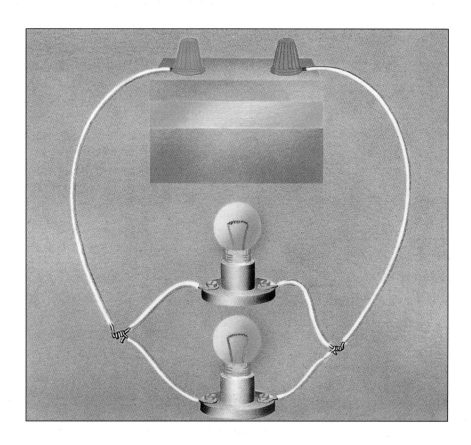

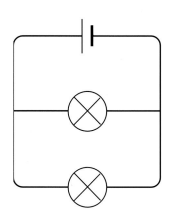

Bulbs (lamps) in parallel

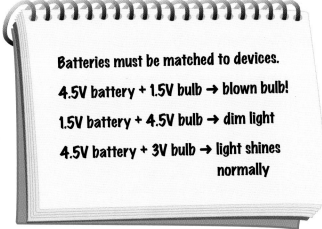

Batteries must be matched to devices.

4.5V battery + 1.5V bulb → blown bulb!

1.5V battery + 4.5V bulb → dim light

4.5V battery + 3V bulb → light shines normally

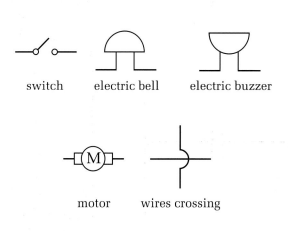

switch   electric bell   electric buzzer

motor   wires crossing

More electrical circuit symbols

 *Reflection*

All electrical circuits are examples of situations in which energy is transferred – for instance, energy stored in the battery is transferred to the bulb or other device.

What is electricity?
Where does electricity come from?
What does it do?

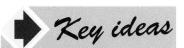

Electrical energy can be produced in power stations and from batteries.

An electrical current is a way of transferring energy.

Energy transferred electrically can be used in different ways to provide lighting and heating, and to make things work.

Electricity can be extremely dangerous.

Children's ideas

Many children imagine electricity to be a sort of fuel that flows into an electrical appliance.

The electrical circuits carrying mains current around our homes are wired up according to the same principles as the simple circuits constructed in a classroom. When we plug in an electrical appliance, we are connecting it into the circuit.

All the appliances in a house are connected in a parallel circuit. This means that each one can be turned on and off by a switch in its own branch of the circuit without affecting the others.

Mains electricity, however, differs from the electricity from a battery in two ways:

- it is much more powerful – mains electricity is supplied at 230 volts in the UK rather than the 1.5 volts of a typical battery;
- it is alternating current (AC for short), so it flows first one way, then the other.

The mains supply uses AC for two reasons. First, it can be produced by simpler machines than those used to generate DC. Second, only AC will work a transformer – a device for changing the voltage of an electricity supply. The ability to transform voltage is essential for the grid of cables on pylons that link power stations to the places where we live. Only by sending the electricity across the country at a very high voltage (such as 400 000 V) is it possible to avoid huge energy losses on the way.

Transformers at power stations raise the supply to a very high voltage for the grid. Other transformers in or near towns lower the voltage again to a relatively safe level for use in our homes.

Electrical hazards

The high voltage of the mains means that the risk of electric shock is serious – 230 V can kill. The severity of a shock depends on the size of the current through your body and the time for which it flows. Modern household circuits include devices that cut off the current at the first sign of a fault that might cause a shock.

A mains shock happens when an electrical current goes through your body into the ground. The supply travels to your home along two wires: the 'live' wire and the 'neutral' wire. The neutral wire is connected to the ground at the transformer, so if you touch the live wire you will complete a circuit via the live wire, your body, the ground and the neutral connection at the power station.

Although your skin does not conduct electricity well, enough current goes through your body to do serious harm. It is much worse if you have wet hands because moisture makes your skin more conductive. The contact between your feet and the ground does not conduct well either, but resistance is lower if the floor is wet. That is why there are strict laws about switches and electric plugs in bathrooms, and why electric mowers and hedge cutters come with fierce warnings about safety. The ground itself offers almost no resistance, not because it is made of good conductors but because it is so enormous.

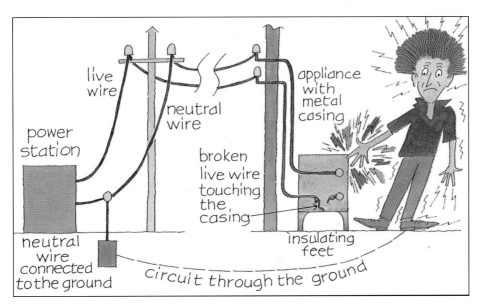

Mains electric shock

Switches: When we switch a light on and off we are closing and opening a gap in the circuit that carries the energy to the light. A mains switch is carefully designed to ensure that the contacts move together and apart quickly and firmly. This reduces electric sparking, which would otherwise soon melt or burn away the metal contacts.

A switch will work no matter where it is in the circuit. However, in mains appliances the switch is always in the live wire (see below). This is for safety. An appliance with its live wire interrupted cannot cause a shock.

It is hazardous if the live wire in an appliance comes loose and touches the casing. Danger can be avoided either by double-insulating the appliance or by earthing the casing. The third wire (coloured green and yellow) in the cable is connected to the casing at one end and to the ground via the plug and household wiring at the other. If the live wire comes loose and touches a metal casing, a massive current flows and blows the fuse in the plug or trips the Earth-leakage circuit breaker. This lessens the risk of a shock and prevents a big current from melting the cable and starting a fire.

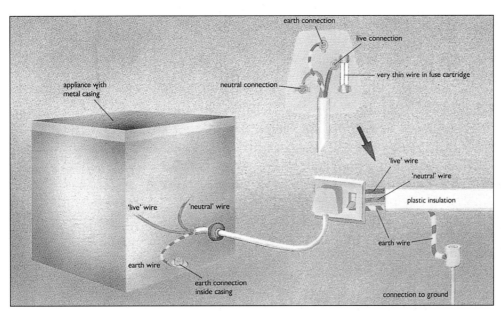

Earthing an appliance

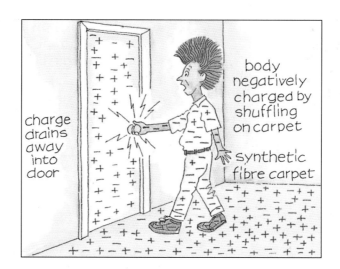

Static electric shock

➤ *Key ideas*

Many objects can become electrically charged even though they are not part of an electrical current.

The electric charge can be moved from place to place and from object to object.

Children's ideas

Some children believe that electricity comes from thunder and lightning, or from the sky.

Children enjoy rubbing balloons against their clothing and then showing that the balloon will cling to the wall or ceiling. A pen rubbed on a sleeve will pick up little fragments of paper. These effects work only if the garment has not been washed with fabric conditioner. Similarly hair may crackle and stand on end when combed in dry weather unless rinsed with conditioner designed to destroy the effect.

These are all effects caused by static electricity but the effect is only noticeable if the charge does not leak away – if it is static, not moving. That is why the effects work better in dry weather. Electric charge trickles away much more easily into moist air, so it cannot build up in damp conditions.

Getting out of a car on a dry day you may get an electric shock as you shut the car door. After walking on a synthetic carpet you can feel the same effect as you turn the door handle. This happens because rubbing on the car seat or the carpet builds up an electric charge on you that discharges through the door when you touch the handle.

Looking inside the particles that make up materials (see pages 42–3) we find that they are made up of even smaller particles with positive and negative charges. Normally the charges cancel each other out. So there is the same number of positive and negative charges and the whole is electrically neutral.

Rubbing two surfaces together can transfer negative electric charges (electrons) from one surface to the other. Then one surface has more negative charges than positive charges and is negative overall. The other surface has a deficit of negative charges and is therefore positive overall.

If the surfaces are made of an insulator such as rubber or plastic, the charges stay put. Opposite charges attract, so a charged balloon seems to stick to the garment it was rubbed against to charge it up. After a while the balloon drops off as the extra charges leak away into the air.

23 ▷ Magnets

How would you decide which of these is a magnet?

Children have fun with magnets – lots of toys use them. There are all sorts of practical uses for magnets too – they help to keep cupboard doors shut and hold up kitchen knives. Magnets play a vital but unseen part in our lives because they are at the heart of all electric motors.

Magnetism can seem very mysterious because we can feel the pull or push of one magnet on another when they are not touching. For most purposes it is enough to know some simple rules about the ways in which magnets can attract and repel each other. Explaining why magnets behave as they do is not easy and beyond the scope of most science books.

Very few metals can be made into strong magnets. Iron, steel, cobalt and nickel can because they have a special internal structure. A simple way of understanding it is to think of each particle (atom) as a little magnet. If the particles are pulled into line, the piece of metal becomes a magnet.

You can magnetize a piece of iron or steel by repeatedly stroking it in one direction with a piece that is already magnetized.

Alternatively you can make a magnet by wrapping a wire around an iron rod and making a current flow in one direction (a DC current) along the wire. The particles in the iron line up because of the magnetic effect produced by the electrical current.

Effects of magnets

The two ends of a magnet are called the north and south poles. The north pole of one magnet attracts the south pole of another, and vice versa. Two north or two south poles repel each other.

The ends of the magnet were given these names because the first practical use of magnets was in a compass. One end of the magnet always points towards the north of the Earth, so this is called the north pole of the magnet. Magnets point north because the Earth is a huge but very weak magnet. Like all magnets, the Earth attracts the opposite pole of other magnets. The south pole of the magnet that is Earth is in northern Canada, very near the geographical North Pole!

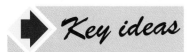

Key ideas

Magnets are made mostly from iron or alloys of iron.

Magnets can attract and repel each other.

Magnets can attract iron and steel objects.

Children's ideas

Children often think that magnets stick to objects because they have magical properties or some kind of glue.

24 ⟩ Sound

How do we hear a knock on the door? How can we tell where it is coming from?

➤ *Key ideas*

Sounds can be high or low, loud or soft.

Sound is caused by vibration in a material.

The amplitude – that is the size – of the vibrations determines the loudness of the sound.

The frequency – that is the number of vibrations each second – determines the pitch of the sound; how high or low it is.

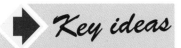

Sounds differ because of

* the number of vibrations per second (the frequency)

* the size of the vibration (the amplitude)

* the material(s) the sound has travelled through.

A knock on a door does not usually cause a movement large enough for the eyes to detect, but it does produce a sound that consists of minute movements in the air. Our ears can detect these. Our brain then receives signals from the ears and is able to gain a great deal of information by analysing this information. What makes this extraordinary sense possible?

Making sound

The impact of knuckles on a door causes the door to vibrate for a moment. These vibrations affect all the substances surrounding the point of impact. (It could be called a 'knock on' effect.) A burst of shock waves travels outwards in all directions from the point of impact, through the wood of the door and through the air. As it passes, it causes the same pattern of vibrations as occurred at the point of impact. The vibrations cause tiny movements in the air, which our ears pick up.

Most sounds are caused by vibrations that have been produced by hitting, plucking, blowing or stroking something.

What makes things sound different?

Frequency, or pitch, is the rate at which the vibrations go backwards and forwards. A small or short instrument vibrates quickly and gives a high note. A large or long instrument vibrates slowly and gives a low note. This applies equally to stringed instruments, organ pipes and terracotta flowerpots. In many cases you can adjust the pitch.

The sound level (amplitude) can be increased by, for instance, hitting a drum harder: this increases the size of the vibration.

Most real sounds, even the sound produced by a musical instrument playing a single note, are a mixture of many vibrations of different amplitudes and frequencies, thus producing a distinctive sound.

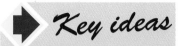

Sound travelling

The producers of space science fiction movies spend millions on graphics and special effects to make their space scenes *look* authentic, but many choose to make their dramas more exciting by making them *sound* inauthentic. As a result, we see spacecraft speeding along against the background of stars making a whoosh or zooming noise. In fact, in Outer Space nothing goes whoosh or zoom. Nothing makes any noise at all. That is because there is no air in Space to carry the vibrations. Without radio communication, the inhabitants of two spacecraft only a few millimetres apart could not hear one another shouting. If the spacecraft touched, though, they could hear. The sound waves could travel through the hull of one craft and into the other.

Sound is the vibration of materials, so sound can only travel through materials. Sound vibrations always have something to travel through on Earth. The sound waves are conducted through air.

However, these waves are not up-and-down waves like those on water. As the vibrating object moves outwards the air is compressed, creating a region of higher pressure than normal. As it moves backwards the air is expanded, so creating a region of lower pressure. Alternate bands of higher and lower pressure air spread out from the object in pulses, and no substance moves from the source to the receiver. These are called sound waves. You can see this idea in the Slinky model at the top of the next page.

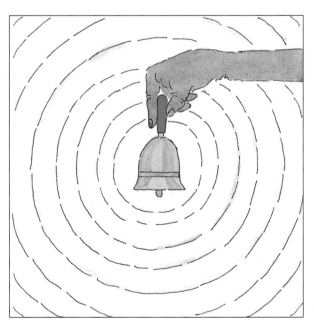

Sound waves radiating from a source

Key ideas

Sound spreads out in all directions.

Sound can be reflected from surfaces and so can produce echoes.

Sound travels through solids, liquids and gases.

Sound travels, and takes a measurable time to do so.

Sound travels as waves, which are vibrations of the substance through which the sound travels.

Children's ideas

Children often have their own ideas about sound travelling, such as 'Tunes are very small and they can get through gaps in the doors.'

Reflection

What is music?

Music is a series of sounds with a recognizable pitch. Musical sound is dominated by a series of steady vibrations at a single frequency, usually accompanied by faster vibrations. These faster vibrations are called overtones. Sound consisting of a random mix of many frequencies is called noise.

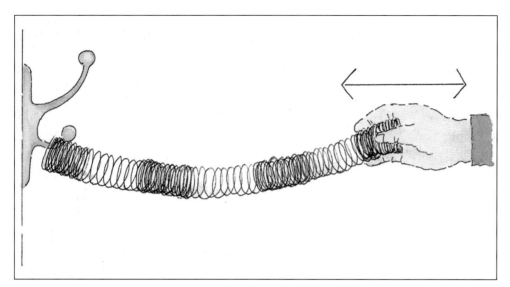

Slinky model of a sound wave

When a sound moves through a material – solid, liquid or gas – the particles (molecules) in the material are made to move backwards and forwards (vibrate) as shown in the diagram on the right. The Slinky spring (above) can show us what this movement is like.

As sound waves travel away from the source of the vibration, the amplitude of the waves become smaller, so the sound gets softer and softer until it is no longer detectable.

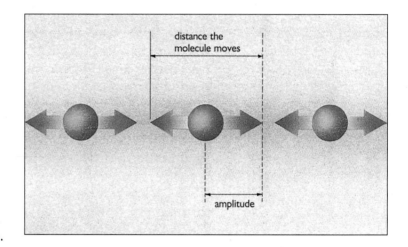

distance the
molecule moves

amplitude

The amplitude of a sound wave

The material that the sound waves travel through also influences the speed at which they travel. In air, sound travels at about 300 metres per second, but it travels more quickly through liquid and faster still in a solid.

Echoes and acoustics

If sound travels better through a solid than through air, why is it that shutting the windows in the classroom reduces the amount of sound coming in from the playground? When sound waves travelling through one material (such as air) encounter a new material (such as the glass of the window), much of the energy of the vibrations is reflected off the surface of second material. Sound waves do travel through the second material but with smaller vibrations (lower amplitude). The sound is therefore less loud. Meanwhile, the sound waves that are reflected off the window travel back out into the playground.

Sound waves that reflect from a surface sometimes produce a discernible second sound, an echo. If you hit a metal dustbin lid with a stick while standing about fifty metres from a brick wall, you will hear the first sound and then hear it again after the sound waves bounce off the wall and come back. This demonstrates that sound waves are reflected. It also shows that it takes time for sound to travel to the wall and back again.

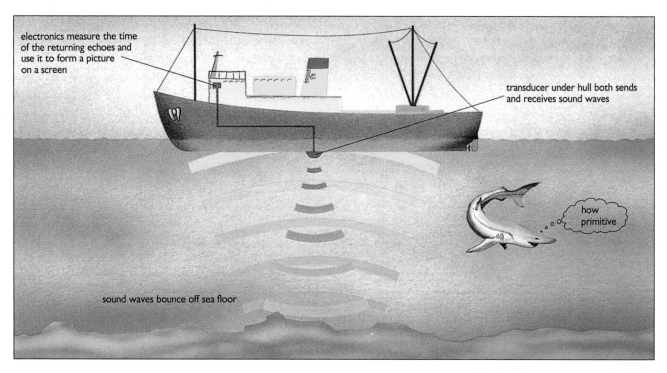

electronics measure the time of the returning echoes and use it to form a picture on a screen

transducer under hull both sends and receives sound waves

how primitive

sound waves bounce off sea floor

Echo sounder

Hard solid surfaces are best for reflecting sound waves, and soft surfaces are good for absorbing sound. Cinemas and theatres often have padded walls and thick carpets to prevent unwanted echoes.

Echoes can be useful. The depth of the sea can be measured by bouncing sound waves off the sea bed. Fishing boats can identify the size and position of a shoal of fish. Dolphins and bats use high-pitched sounds to locate objects in the dark.

> ▶ *Key idea*
>
> Sound can be detected by sensitive instruments, which include the human ear.

Hearing sounds

You are settling down to relax for the evening when your next-door neighbour's child decides it is time to practise the violin. How can you hear the sound?

All devices that receive sound, including our ears, detect the vibrations in some way and then process them.

We hear because the outer ear collects the sound waves made by the vibrating object and carries them to the eardrum, which is a thin stretched membrane.

The eardrum vibrates, causing further vibrations in the bones inside the ear. The last of these bones (the stirrup) causes the fluid in the cochlea to vibrate and stimulate the nerves, which then transmit the message to the brain. The brain identifies the pattern of the information that comes from both ears and is able to help us identify the sound and where it came from.

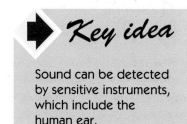

outer ear

hammer (malleus)

anvil (incus)

semi-circular canal

stirrup (stapes)
oval window

nerve to brain

cochlea

ear canal

eardrum

middle ear chamber

round window

earbones (natural size)

Eustachian tube

The structure of the ear

How would you explain how we see an object, such as this book?

Children's ideas

Children often think that we see a book because light travels from our eyes to the book.

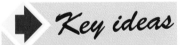

Key ideas

Light comes from a variety of sources: primary sources, which give out light directly; and secondary sources, which reflect light.

Objects can be seen because they either give out or reflect light.

Objects are seen when light enters the eye.

Sources of light

We see stars in the night sky because, like the Sun, they radiate light. They are primary sources of light, as are glowing embers, light bulbs, flames and a TV screen.

We see the Moon at night, not because it radiates its own light, but because it reflects light from the Sun (see page 88). The Moon is a secondary source, as are most of the objects we see by daylight, as well as the images on a projector screen or a patch of road picked out in a headlight beam.

Seeing the light

Some people think that we see with our eyes actively and that our eyes give off some kind of sight rays that select the object of our attention. Even our language reflects this idea: we 'look daggers', 'cast our gaze' and 'peer through'.

The scientific understanding is the exact opposite of this. We see objects because light reflected from the object enters our eyes. No rays leave our eyes. Our eyes are active in the sense that we have to direct our vision to the point of interest, and that the lens adjusts to form an image on the retina of the light that comes into the eyes. Also the coloured iris opens and closes according to the brightness of the incoming light, making the pupil larger or smaller.

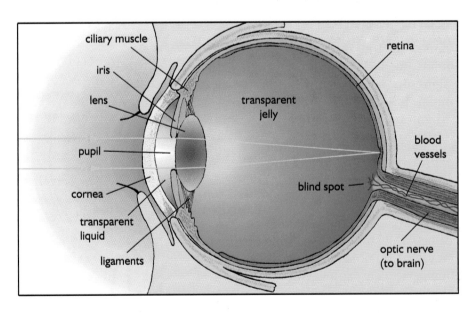

The structure of the eye

What is light?

Scientists use two main theories to explain what light is like. In some ways light behaves like a wave. In other ways light is like a stream of packets of energy. These ideas are used to explain the different colours and what happens when light is reflected and refracted (see the pictures on the following pages).

Reflection: You can see objects reflected in the water (see also page 80).

Refraction: If you look through the water at objects under water, they appear to be in a different position from where they actually are, because the light is bent when it passes from water to air. This bending is called refraction.

Light waves are very different from sound waves (see page 75). They move about a million times faster and can travel through a vacuum. The light we can see belongs to the big family of types of radiation that includes X-rays, ultra-violet light, microwaves and radio waves. All these types of waves stream out of the Sun, but most of them are filtered out by the atmosphere. The gas ozone, for example, filters out most of the dangerous ultra-violet light that causes eye damage, severe sunburn and cancer.

What distinguishes one type of radiation from another is the number of waves passing by per second – the frequency. Just as a radio can be tuned to receive the right frequency for a particular broadcasting station, so our eyes are 'tuned' to detect the narrow band of sunlight that can get through the atmosphere and light up the surface of the Earth.

Our eyes cannot detect all the light from the Sun. We feel the warmth of infra-red rays in summer but we cannot see by these rays except with the help of a specially designed camera that can detect a wider range of frequencies than our eyes.

Seeing colour

Most animals do not see in colour. The picture of the world they perceive is based only on the brightness or dimness of light, a bit like a black and white photograph. Our night vision is like this. In very dim light, the only cells of the retina sensitive enough for seeing are the rods, and they cannot distinguish colours.

We see in colour in daylight because there are three other types of sensitive cells (the cones) in our retinas. One type responds to red light, another to green, and the third to blue light.

What effects of light can you see in this picture?

How would you explain
- **how a shadow is formed?**
- **what a reflection is?**

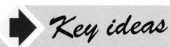

Key ideas

Light travels through some materials but not through others.

The position, shape and size of a shadow depend upon the position of the object in relation to the position of the light source.

Light is scattered off objects.

Light travels in straight lines.

When we open the bedroom curtains, light seems to fill the room instantly. Light travels so quickly that our eyes and brains cannot perceive it coming into the window and moving around the room. However, the light interacts with objects in different ways.

- **Transparent materials:** Light travels through transparent materials such as the glass of the window and the air of the room.

- **Opaque materials:** The bed, floor and walls are made of opaque materials. When light encounters these materials, some is absorbed, and some bounces off the material and scatters in all directions. This is the reason light seems to fill a room. The light that shines into a room hits opaque materials and is scattered all over the room. This is how we see opaque materials.

- **Reflective materials:** The dressing table mirror contains reflective material. This kind of material absorbs only a small amount of the energy of the light. Most of the light that hits the surface of the material is reflected. This means that it bounces off the surface and travels away at exactly the same angle as it travelled towards it.

This is different from the scattering of light, which happens when light shines on a rough surface. Light bouncing off a rough surface behaves like a handful of ball-bearings thrown onto a cobbled street. The light bounces off in all directions.

Light bouncing off a mirror behaves like a ball bouncing off a smooth wall. The light that hits the mirror straight on bounces back exactly where it came from. The light that hits it at an angle bounces off at that same angle but on the opposite side.

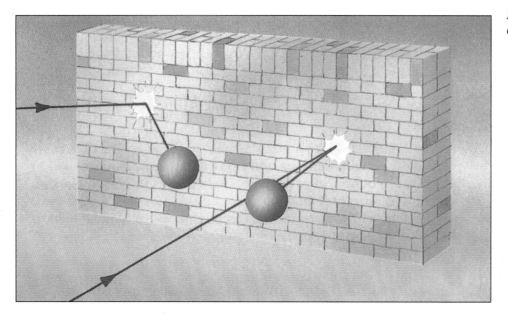

Model of light hitting a mirror

- **Shadows:** On the dressing table is a bottle of hand lotion and on the window sill is a flower pot. The bottle casts a shadow because it is made of opaque plastic that blocks the light travelling towards it. The opaque flowerpot also casts a shadow. The area of the shadow is darker than the surrounding area but it is not completely dark. Some light scattered from other parts of the room reaches the shadow areas of the table top and window sill.

- **Translucent materials:** The light passing through the roller blind is of reduced intensity, because some is reflected back, and some is scattered and therefore appears more diffuse. Materials that behave like the blind, allowing light to shine through but scattering it as it passes, are known as translucent materials.

 Children's ideas

Children are very confused about shadows and reflections, as this example shows.

'I think a shadow is a reflection from the Sun. Sometimes when you look in a pond you see a reflection. When you go somewhere where it can reflect you see your shadow.'

Why are leaves green?

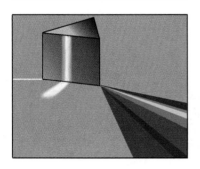

Key ideas

Different colours can be created by mixing coloured paints or by using filters.

White light can be split into different colours.

Light shining through a prism

Mixing coloured light:
red + green = yellow

Mixing coloured paint:
red + green = brown

Rainbows

Light from the Sun consists of many colours. We commonly know these as the colours of the rainbow – red, orange, yellow, green, blue, indigo and violet.

Different colours of light are bent by different amounts as they pass into a transparent material. We sense different frequencies of light waves as different colours. Red, which has the lowest frequency, bends least, and violet, with the highest frequency, bends most. The shape of the glass affects how much we notice this bending. When we look through a pane of window glass with its smooth parallel sides, all the light reaches our eyes undistorted and we see white light.

When light shines into a piece of glass in the shape of a triangular prism, however, it emerges with the different frequencies bent by different amounts. So when white light shines into such a prism, it emerges as a fan of light with the red light, which is bent the least, on one end of the fan, the violet on the other end of the fan, and the colours of the rainbow spread out in between.

Rainbows in the sky are produced in a similar way when drops of water (raindrops) in the air bend and reflect the light from the Sun.

Colour and opaque objects

We perceive the world around us as coloured because it contains objects made of opaque materials that absorb some light frequencies and scatter others.

The pigments in paints absorb some colours and scatter, or reflect, others: the pigment in red paint absorbs blue, yellow and green light but scatters red light.

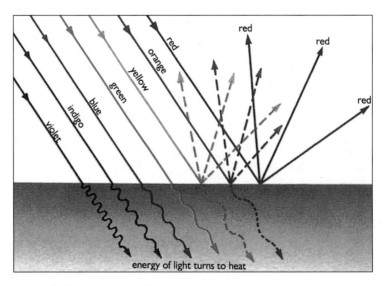

White light hitting a red object

The natural landscape is largely green because plants absorb light energy in order to photosynthesize (see pages 11–12) but they do not absorb green light. They absorb blue and violet light and red light. The light in the middle range is scattered off the surface of the leaves and this is the light we see as green. If leaves absorbed all the light from the Sun and scattered none, they would look black.

Colour filters

Materials that are transparent, such as glass, water and air, allow light to travel through. If they are colourless, they allow light of all frequencies to pass through. If a substance that absorbs light of certain frequencies is added to these materials, the light that emerges from the material then appears coloured. This is because it has had some of the frequencies removed, not because colour is added. For example, the craftsmen who made the windows of the great medieval cathedrals created masterpieces of coloured light by adding metal oxides to glass when it was molten. Adding iron oxide made the glass look green because all the colours except green were absorbed as the light passed through the glass. Adding copper oxide made red glass and adding cobalt made blue glass.

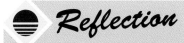
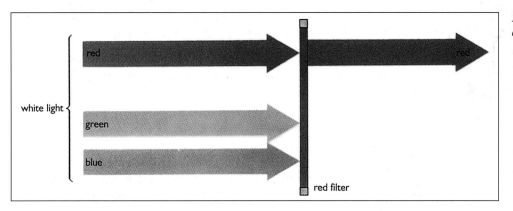

How coloured glass acts as a filter

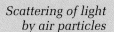

Blue skies

Children often ask why the sky is blue: the answer is hard for them to grasp.

Light from the Sun is scattered in all directions by the particles of the air. We detect the light that is scattered downwards. The light from the blue end of the spectrum is scattered more than the light from the red end, so we see the sky as blue.

The red light passes through the atmosphere largely unscattered, so we see the Sun with an orangy-yellow colour, having lost its blue.

Scattering of light by air particles

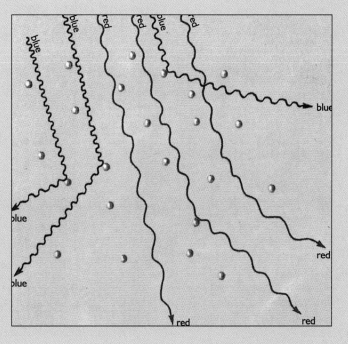

Children's ideas

Children often do not relate the colours they see to the materials the objects are made of.

83

What kind of heavenly bodies are there in our Solar System?

Planets

The Earth and its Moon are not the only heavenly bodies that orbit the Sun. There are eight other planets, many of which have moons orbiting them. Between the orbit of Mars and Jupiter, a ring of boulders of irregular size and shape travels around the Sun. These are the asteroids.

Meteors

Also orbiting the Sun are many smaller chunks of rock. It is these that create the meteors, or 'shooting stars', we occasionally see. When a chunk of rock gets close enough to the Earth to be pulled in by its gravity, it accelerates very rapidly to the ground. Friction between the air of the atmosphere and the surface of the rock makes it get hot and glow. As the rock gets hotter, it begins to vaporize. It rapidly gets smaller as it approaches the ground and only the largest make it to the ground before evaporating completely. Those that do hit ground are travelling so quickly that they blast a hole, a crater, at the point of impact. The rocks that arrive on Earth in this way are called meteorites.

Comets

Comets are also occasional visitors to the night sky. These are dusty lumps of rock and ice that come tumbling towards the Sun from far out in Space, well beyond the orbit of Pluto. Most of them just crash into the Sun and vaporize, but occasionally, as with Halley's comet, they will miss the Sun, swing round, go hurtling out into Space again and return on a regular basis.

Sun and other stars

The Sun is a star, an ordinary, medium-sized, middle-aged star. It only looks bigger and brighter than the other stars because it is very much closer. The light from the Sun takes eight minutes to reach the Earth. The light from the next nearest star takes over four years to reach us. The Sun is one of a hundred thousand million stars that make up the Milky Way Galaxy. The Milky Way is one of the billions of galaxies that make up the Universe.

Children's ideas

It is not self-evident that the Earth is a planet orbiting the Sun. We notice the Sun's apparent movement across the sky each day and talk about the Sun 'rising', 'coming up', 'going down', 'going behind the clouds', all of which imply that it is the Sun rather than the Earth that is moving.

Children may tell their teacher that the Earth is round, but their responses to questions often show that they really consider it to be flat.

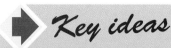
Key ideas

The Earth is one of the nine planets in our Solar System, all of which orbit the Sun.

The Sun is a star at the centre of our Solar System.

The stars – apart from the Sun – are far outside the Solar System.

The stars look as if they are in groups, which we call constellations.

The planets in our Solar System

Name	Distance from Sun (millions of km)	Time for orbit	Diameter (km)	Number of moons
Mercury	58	88 days	4 820	0
Venus	108	225 days	12 103	0
Earth	150	1 year	12 756	1
Mars	228	1.9 years	6 794	2
Jupiter	780	12 years	142 800	16
Saturn	1 430	29 years	120 660	17
Uranus	2 870	84 years	51 400	15
Neptune	4 500	165 years	49 400	8
Pluto	5 900	248 years	2 280	1

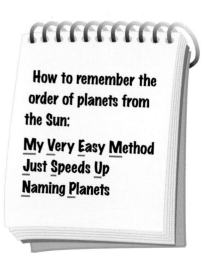

How to remember the order of planets from the Sun:

My Very Easy Method Just Speeds Up Naming Planets

The Universe

Astronomers, using telescopes that detect different kinds of radiation from Space, have found that nearly all the galaxies are moving away from one another. From this, they have concluded that the Universe is expanding, which led them to suggest that the whole Universe may have grown from a single point in Space in an enormous 'Big Bang' explosion that happened about fifteen thousand million years ago.

Gravity

Children sometimes say that there is no gravity on the Moon, or that things will float away on the Moon because there is no air to hold them down.

Many children are fascinated with the idea of being weightless or being able to soar around like Superman. Gravity is the force that keeps us 'down to Earth'. It's a real 'downer'. It makes us fall and hurt ourselves. Can we improve gravity's image? Gravity is one of the fundamental forces that makes the Universe what it is. (See also 'Forces and movement' on pages 54–7.)

Newton realized that the force he called gravity does not just make things fall to Earth. It explains the behaviour of the Moon as it orbits the Earth, and the planets as they orbit the Sun.

Gravity is a force of attraction that is related to the mass of an object. Massive objects attract each other strongly. Objects with small mass attract each other very weakly. There is a gravitational attraction between all objects because they all have mass. For example, there is a gravitational attraction between you and the person next to you, but you cannot feel it because it is so small.

The Moon is less massive than the Earth so the pull of the Moon's gravity is weaker than that of Earth (about one-sixth). That is why the astronauts who visited the Moon were able to jump around so easily despite their heavy space suits.

The picture at the top of the next page shows the effect of gravity on a thrown ball on Earth.

If the same ball were thrown in Outer Space it would just keep moving away at the same speed until it disappeared from view. That is because the forces operating in Outer Space are different. There is no air to slow down the ball's movement and the gravity from distant stars and planets would have little or no influence on its movement.

 Reflection

Recognizing the effects of gravity is comparatively easy. Explaining what gravity is is far beyond the scope of this book.

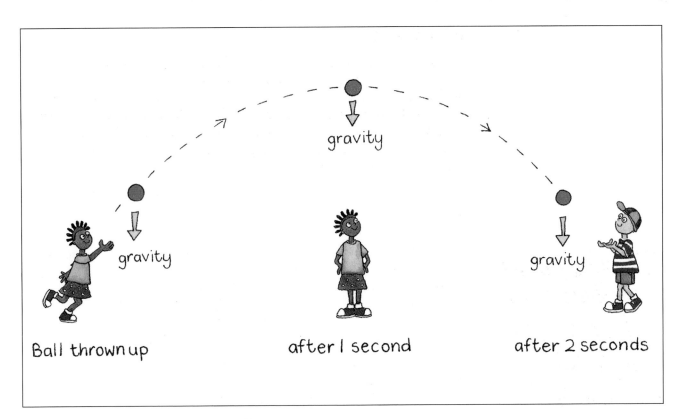

The main forces acting on a thrown ball

Why a satellite stays in orbit round a planet

The orbit of a planet, moon or other satellite is controlled by gravity and the tendency of a moving object to continue in a straight line. A small thought experiment may help make this clear.

Imagine that you are on a planet with a cannon. Put a small charge in the cannon and fire it. The ball follows a short curved path as gravity pulls it to the ground. Use a larger charge: the ball goes quite a way around the planet before it hits the ground. With a larger charge still, the curve takes the ball right round the planet. If there is no air resistance to slow it, it will orbit the planet for ever.

A cannon ball ejected in this way would have to go round very fast to stay in orbit. The further away from the planet it is the more slowly it need go, because the pull of gravity is weaker.

When rocket engineers send up a satellite to orbit the Earth, they send it up to the height they want, giving it just the right speed so that it will orbit the Earth and not fly off into Space or fall to the ground.

Astronauts in a spacecraft orbiting the Earth are falling round the Earth at the same rate as the spacecraft. So they do not press on the floor of the spacecraft and this gives the impression that they are weightless. When their mission is over, they can use spacecraft's rockets to slow them down, and the Earth's gravity will pull them home.

Thought experiment with a cannon

87

The phases of the Moon

The Moon shines with reflected light from the Sun (see page 78).

The Moon appears to change shape as it orbits the Earth because, as it moves, light from the Sun shines on different parts of its surface. We can often see only part of the side with sunlight on it.

New Moon: When we see a new Moon the sunlight is falling on the side facing away from us – see top left.

The Moon appears to be in darkness when it is new because the Sun is shining on the back side, not because the Earth is in the way.

Full Moon: When we see a full Moon we see the sunlight shining on the side of the Moon facing us – see bottom left.

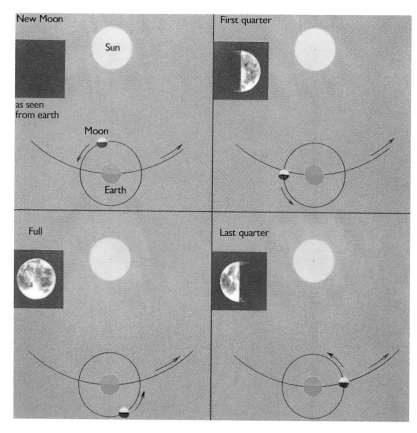

The phases of the Moon

First and last quarters: During the first and last quarters, half of the side of the Moon facing us has sunlight falling on it and half does not – see top right and bottom right.

We always see the same side of the Moon facing us (see the diagram below). This is because the Moon is spinning on its axis at the same rate as it is orbiting the Earth.

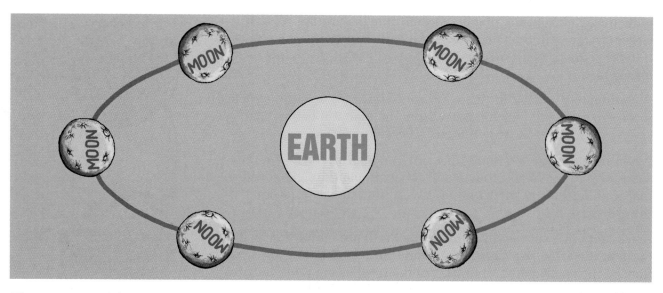

The movement of the Moon round the Earth in the course of a month

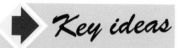
29 Measuring time

Our measurement of time is related to planetary motion. How you would explain one day, one month and one year?

Long before people had any idea that the Earth is a sphere that travels around the Sun, they were acute observers of the movements of the 'heavenly bodies'. The clock and calendar we use today have developed over the centuries based on the relative movements of the Earth, Sun and Moon.

- The Earth spins on its axis.

- The Moon goes round the Earth.

- The Earth goes round the Sun.

▶ *Key ideas*

It takes a day, 24 hours, for the Earth to spin around once.

It takes one year, 365¼ days, for the Earth to orbit the Sun.

Measurement of time is related to the relative movements and positions of the Earth, Sun and Moon.

The Earth spins and the Moon goes around it.

Night occurs because the Earth spins. At any time half the Earth is illuminated by the Sun (day-time), and the other half is in shadow (night-time).

Children's ideas

Young children may say that night happens because we need to sleep, because the Sun swaps with the Moon, or because the Sun has gone to Australia.

Days

Only the side of Earth that faces the Sun is light but, because the Earth spins, every part of the world gets its share of sunlight. A day, or 24 hours, is the time it takes for the Earth to make one complete revolution, taking a point on the Earth from the dark to the light and into the dark again. The ancient Babylonians split the day into the smaller units we use today. A day has 24 hours. An hour has 60 minutes. A minute has 60 seconds.

Months

The Moon is another spherical body about one-fiftieth the size of the Earth. It constantly orbits (travels a roughly circular route around) the Earth. It takes the Moon about 28 days to orbit the Earth. The Moon goes from one full Moon to the next about every 29½ days. (The difference is because the Earth and Moon are also moving round the Sun.)

Twelve lunar months is about 354 days, which is close to one year. From this has arisen the practice of dividing the year into 12 months – the exact number of days in each month varies and makes up a complete year.

30 Seasonal change

Why are days longer in summer?

We experience seasons because of the tilt of the Earth, not because of any variation in the Earth's distance from the Sun. It is true that this does vary a little, but other factors are more important. In fact, the Earth is closer to the Sun during the northern winter than it is during the summer.

The Earth spins around an imaginary line, called its axis, which runs straight through the centre of the Earth, from the North Pole to the South Pole. This line is slightly tilted with respect to the path the Earth takes as it orbits the Sun. It is this tilt that causes the seasons and changing hours of daylight on Earth.

When the Earth is on one side of the Sun, the northern half of the Earth is tilted towards the Sun and the southern half is tilted away. This means that the northern hemisphere gets extra sunshine – see the diagram at the bottom of the next page. There is daylight for a greater proportion of the day and, because the Sun is shining more directly on the northern hemisphere, the north receives more intense sunshine. More light and heat energy pour onto this part of the Earth. The Sun reaches higher in the sky and the days are longer. This is, of course, the time of year that people in the north

Why day length varies

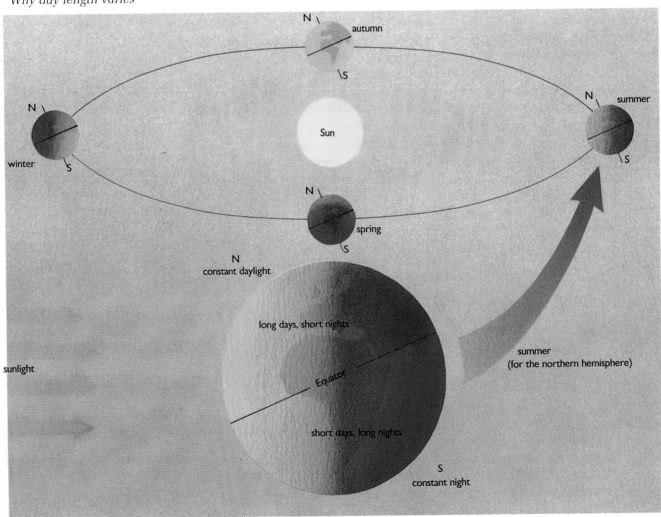

call summer. At the same time, in the southern hemisphere, it is winter. It's colder and the nights are longer.

Six months later, however, the Earth has travelled around to the opposite side of the Sun and now it is the southern hemisphere that is tilted toward the Sun. It is summer in Australia and winter in Europe.

Generally, the parts of the Earth that are closer to the North or South Pole experience more extreme seasonal changes than parts that are closer to the Equator. During the northern summer, an area around the North Pole has permanent daylight. Instead of rising or setting, the Sun just travels all the way around the horizon – hence the term 'land of the midnight sun'. As you travel toward the Equator, the difference in the length of daylight between winter and summer is less and less extreme.

The climate of different parts of the Earth is also influenced by other factors such as the height above sea level and the nearness to the sea. The mildness of British winters is due to the Gulf Stream, a current of warm water that travels northeastwards from the Caribbean and warms the waters around Britain and the coast of Europe.

It takes time for land and air to warm up and cool down, so the seasons we experience happen later than one would predict from the length of day. The longest day, 21 or 22 June, is the day when the Sun is highest in the northern sky and the sunlight most intense, but most areas in the north experience their warmest weather in July and August.

Key ideas

The seasons are caused by the tilt of the Earth. Winter happens on that part of the Earth that is tilted away from the Sun.

The tilt makes the days shorter and reduces the amount of sunlight that falls on that part of the Earth's surface, so the weather is colder.

Reflection

The effect of the tilt in winter is shorter days and a reduction in the amount of sunlight per unit area, so the weather is colder.

In summer the tilt causes longer days and an increase in the amount of sunlight per unit area, so the weather is warmer.

Why summer is hot and winter is cold

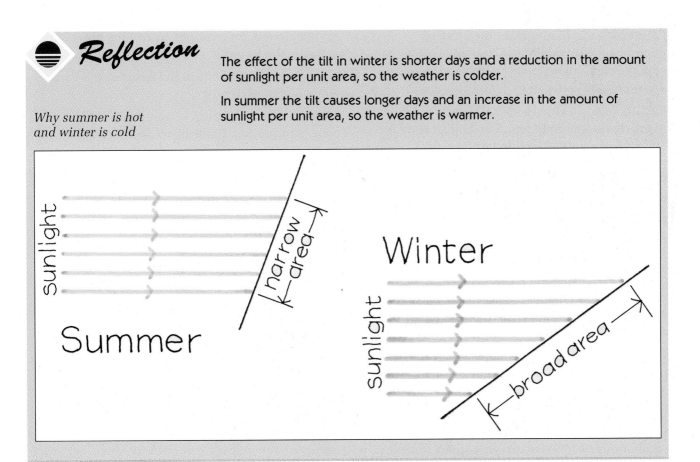

Glossary

Acid Acids are sour, sharp-tasting substances found in many living things, for example, citric acid, which gives oranges and lemons their sharp flavour. Acids have a pH of less than 7.

Alkali Alkalis are substances that neutralize acids. Alkalis have a pH of more than 7.

Amplitude Amplitude refers to the size of a vibration. The amplitude of a sound wave determines the loudness of the sound. The greater the amplitude the louder the sound.

Anther The part of a flower where pollen develops.

Arteries Arteries are muscular tubes that carry blood from the heart to the rest of the body. They branch and branch, forming much smaller tubes, and finally becoming a web of microscopically small tubes called capillaries.

Asteroid Asteroids are a ring of boulders of irregular size and shape, most of which travel around the Sun between the orbit of Mars and Jupiter.

Bacteria Bacteria are microscopic organisms that consist of single cells much smaller than animal or plant cells.

Capillaries Capillaries make up a web of microscopically small tubes branching off from arteries, then linking up to carry blood to veins. There are capillaries in most body tissues.

Cell Biological cells are the basic units of which living things are composed. The human body is made up of about 100 million million cells. In electricity, 'cell' is another word for 'battery'. 'Battery' is strictly the collective noun for a group of cells.

Cellulose Cellulose is a substance made up of long chains of sugar molecules linked together with strong bonds. It forms a main part of plant cell walls.

Chlorophyll Chlorophyll makes leaves green. It is found in chloroplasts in the cells and plays a key role in photosynthesis.

Comets Comets are dusty lumps of rock and ice that orbit the Sun, travelling well beyond the orbit of Pluto. Some, such as Halley's comet, return on a regular basis.

Consumers Organisms (such as animals and carnivorous plants) that eat other living things.

Decomposers Organisms that consume the dead remains or waste products of other living things.

Density Density measures the mass of a material in relation to its size. Density is calculated by dividing the mass of a sample of a material by its volume.

DNA DNA, or deoxyribonucleic acid, is a chemical found in cells that carries coded instructions, known as the genetic information. This determines how the organism grows and develops. The instructions are divided into units of information called genes.

Ecosystem The word ecosystem is used when talking about the community of living organisms together with their habitat. Many components interact to form an ecosystem.

Electricity The term 'electricity' can have several meanings. It can mean electric charge, electric current, or the energy transferred by electric charge. Current electricity is a flow of electric charges through a conductor. Static electricity is a build-up of charge on an insulator such as a plastic rod rubbed against clothing.

Energy Energy is needed to generate the forces that make things work or go. This happens when energy is transferred, for example, by heating or by forces making things move.

Evolution The change in life forms over a very long period of time.

Force A force is a push or a pull applied by one object to another. Force is needed to change the movement of an object – to start it moving, speed it up, slow it down, stop it from moving or change its direction. Forces also change the shape of objects by compressing, stretching or shearing them.

Frequency Frequency is the number of vibrations per second. The frequency of a sound wave determines the pitch of a sound. The greater the frequency the higher the pitch.

Friction Friction is a force that opposes the movement of one surface across another.

Gene A unit of genetic information found in DNA.

Genetic information The entire blueprint for an organism, that is, the information on how to grow and develop, is known as its genetic information. This information is coded into the structure of the chemical found in the cells called deoxyribonucleic acid, or DNA for short.

Gravity Gravity is a force of attraction that is related to the mass of the objects and the distance between them. There is a gravitational attraction between all objects because they all have mass. The larger the masses the greater the attraction. The greater the distance between objects the smaller the attraction.

Habitat The place in which an organism lives.

Igneous rocks Igneous rocks, such as granite and basalt, are formed by the cooling of molten material. The size of the mineral crystals depends on the rate of cooling. The faster the molten material cools, the smaller the crystals.

Inertia If nothing stops it, an object will keep moving if it is moving, or remain stationary if it is stationary. This is inertia. In other words, a large moving object will take more force to stop it or start it moving than a small one.

Mass Mass is the amount of matter something is made of. It is also a measure of how much force you need to speed an object up or slow it down. The mass of a body does not depend on where you are (Earth, Moon, or anywhere else) even though its weight (the pull of gravity) can change a lot.

Material The word 'material', as used in this book, includes all the substances things are made from – metals, ceramics, plastics and wood – as well as the flesh and blood of our own bodies.

Metamorphic rock Metamorphic rock forms when a rock is changed by intense heat and/or pressure. For example, shale can be turned into slate, and limestone into marble.

Meteors Meteors, or 'shooting stars', are small chunks of rock orbiting the Sun that get close enough to the Earth to be pulled in by its gravity and accelerate into the atmosphere where they heat up and vaporize. The rocks that arrive on Earth are called meteorites.

Mutation A mistake in the genetic information passed from parent to offspring. Mutations cause major variations between different individuals within a species.

Natural selection Natural selection means that those individuals best suited to the environment are most likely to survive and so pass their genes on to the next generation.

Newton A newton is a unit of measure for force. For example, the pull of gravity on an object (weight) is 1 newton on a 100-gram mass. So the pull of gravity on an apple is about 1 newton.

Nutrients Living things need to take in certain materials that are essential to the construction of their cellular machinery. These are known as nutrients and normally include vitamins and minerals.

Opaque Light does not shine through opaque materials.

Ovule Ovules contain a plant's female reproductive cell. The ovary of a plant is part of the flower and contains one or more ovules. When an ovule is pollinated, it develops into a seed.

Particle Materials are made up of particles, that is, atoms and molecules. The word 'particle' can also be used to mean a small speck such as a speck of dust.

Photosynthesis This is a series of chemical reactions that uses light energy to bind chemicals together. Photosynthesis allows plants to get energy from light.

Pitch Pitch is determined by the frequency of a sound wave. The higher the frequency, the higher the pitch of the note.

Pollen Pollen grains form in the anther of a flower. Each grain contains a male nucleus that can fertilize an egg cell in an ovule to produce a seed.

Pollination Pollination occurs after pollen lands on the stigma of a plant of the same species. The genetic information in the pollen then joins with the genetic information of an egg cell in an ovule to create a fertilized cell with a new combination. This develops into a seed.

Pressure Pressure is a measure of how much force is being applied to a certain area. High pressures are caused by a large force on a small area, such as stiletto heels. Low pressures are caused by increasing the area, such as snow shoes, or lowering the force.

Producers Living things that get energy by photosynthesis.

Reflection Reflection occurs when most of the light that hits the surface of a material bounces off the surface again.

Refraction If you look through the water at objects under water, they appear to be in a different position from where they actually are. This is because the light rays change direction when passing from water to air. This bending is an example of refraction.

Resistance Air resistance is the interference with the movement of an object through air. Electrical resistance is a measure of the difficulty of the flow of electrical current through a material.

Respiration Respiration is the chemical process that occurs in cells to release energy from food and oxygen. During respiration the cell takes in food (especially sugars) and oxygen, and produces carbon dioxide and water.

Sedimentary rock Sedimentary rocks, such as limestone and sandstone, are formed as a result of fragments that have settled, usually under water, and then compacted into rocks when buried and compressed.

Solution A solution is formed when a substance such as sugar, the solute, has dissolved in another substance such as water, the solvent. When a solute dissolves in solvent it mixes perfectly and the resulting solution is transparent, though it may be coloured.

Stigma The part of a flower, associated with the ovule, that catches pollen.

Suspension A suspension is formed when grains of a substance such as sand are suspended in a fluid such as water. Suspensions are cloudy because the solid specks reflect and scatter light.

Temperature Temperature is a measure of how hot a substance is.

Translucent The light passing through a translucent material is of reduced intensity, as some is reflected back, and some is scattered and therefore appears more diffuse. You can't see through it.

Transparent Materials that are transparent, such as glass, water and air, allow light to travel through. If they are colourless, they allow light of all frequencies to pass through. You can see through them.

Upthrust Upthrust is the force that pushes up on an object in water, or any other liquid or gas. Upthrust counteracts the force of gravity.

Veins The tubes that carry blood away from body tissues (see capillaries). Veins converge to form bigger and bigger veins and finally carry the blood back to the heart.

Virus Viruses are packages of genetic material. They invade living cells and are then able to multiply, killing the cell. They can then infect other cells. In humans, viruses cause diseases such as HIV or influenza.

Voltage Voltage is a measure of the amount of energy given to the electrical charges that flow round a circuit.

Volume Volume is the amount of space an object takes up.

Weight Weight is a force. It is the pull of gravity on an object. Weight is measured in newtons. On Earth the pull of gravity is 10 newtons on each kilogram mass.

Index